The Biology of Human Destiny **DOMINANT**

St Martin's Press, New Yor

Sir Macfarlane Burnet

MAMMAL

For my grandchildren
Sue, Jenny, Robin, Jeremy, David, Andrew and Michael
May they see and enjoy the twenty-first century

CONTENTS

ACKNOWLEDGEMENTS

I am grateful to Mr Arthur Koestler for sending me a copy of his address on The Predicament of Man, from which the excerpt on page 73 is taken.

In addition, for granting permission to reprint otherwise copyright material, the publishers wish to acknowledge the author and Messrs Angus & Robertson Limited for an extract from *Flying Fox and Drifting Sand* by Francis Ratcliffe (page 180); the author and the McGraw-Hill Book Company for an extract from *Animal Behaviour* by Robert A. Hinde (page 48); and Messrs Pergamon Press Australia for an extract from *Immunological Surveillance* by Macfarlane Burnet (page 35).

LIST OF FIGURES

one INTRODUCTION

At the age of seventy, I find myself an elderly medical scientist with a considerable record of achievement and recognition. I have shared a Nobel Prize, there is an important agent of human infection called *Rickettsia* (*Coxiella*) *burneti*, and in the literature of immunology there are four phrases often used, 'self and not-self', 'clonal selection', 'forbidden clones' and 'immunological surveillance', which I can claim to have introduced in that particular context. Presumably, this indicates that I have the sort of intelligence, drive and 'creativity' appropriate to an experimental scientist, plus a taste for, and some competence in scientific generalization about biological matters.

I am completely aware of the immensely greater complexity of human problems than any that we can tackle in the laboratory. But man *is* a species of mammal, and for at least the last thirty years I have repeatedly tried to apply an understanding of biology to human affairs. In the first instance, the problems that interested me were ecological ones: how epidemic disease spread in a human population, at what ages it killed, and how, by manipulating the environment, the disease might sometimes be eliminated. There are many infectious diseases of man the natural history of which involves other species of animal. Yellow fever persists in the Amazonian jungles because the virus is carried by the mosquitoes of the forest canopy from monkey to monkey, until wood-cutters or other jungle-workers intrude almost accidentally into the cycle. From these, urban epidemics in which only man and the *Aedes* mosquito are involved may result. The complexities of malaria and its control are endless, even if only man,

Anopheline mosquitoes and the malarial parasites are concerned. There are dozens of such complex ecological situations involving human disease, two of which, psittacosis and Murray Valley encephalitis, I have studied in the Australian environment. In all of them, the ecological approach must be applied as much to man as to any of the other organisms involved in the epidemiology of disease. Infectious disease in man is the same sort of mutual interaction of two or more organisms as any of the oscillating equilibria between predator and prey on the African plains or in the depths of the sea. I suspect that the whole science of ecology—the interaction of organisms with their environment—developed and became respectable because of its importance in the understanding of the two classical plagues of the tropics, malaria and yellow fever.

There was the intellectual background here for the development of a special interest in human ecology. That interest was probably accentuated by an inborn shyness, a harmless terror of strangers, that may have made it easier for me to stand off and look at human beings as just another species of mammal than it would have been for an outgoing extrovert.

From the early 1940s, I have never been able wholly to live in the ivory tower of scholarly activity. I became director of a research institute and almost automatically found myself involved in the inevitable problems of administration and in committee activities. In the period immediately after the Second World War (1946–50), I was a member of three official Australian committees concerned with scientific research. The most important was the initial Defence Research Committee, under the chairmanship of A. P. Rowe. In those committees I was not very effective, and for the most part confined my remarks strictly to matters of which I had technical knowledge. But, internally, I was both lifted up by the feeling that I was concerned with important matters and worried about the lack of any but short-term approaches to the problems which concerned those committees.

I believe that it was this experience which sparked off a serious interest in the human situation as looked at from the biological angle, particularly in regard to those problems from the wider world which came to trouble me—war and over-population especially.

Human biology was not a phrase of the 1940s. There was plenty of academic discussion on the population problem, but it was not taken as a political or social reality. In all advanced countries the upper- and middle-classes practised birth control with relatively primitive techniques and were worried, at times, that Roman Catholics, negroes or the working-classes would outbreed them. The whole outlook on war was changed when the bombs were dropped on Hiroshima and Nagasaki, but attempts to understand human conflict in terms of the scientifically accessible phenomena of animal behaviour were still embryonic. Peck-order in chickens was the only topic that had come into common biological knowledge, and no one had begun to write books about aggression, or to talk of man as a naked ape. I read what I could find about peck-orders, about the behaviour of baboons on Monkey Hill in the London Zoo, and anything else that seemed relevant. Gradually, the idea of writing a book about man as a mammal grew upon me.

There were quite a lot of things to push me in that direction. In 1940, I had published my first book, *Biological Aspects of Infectious Diseases*. It is a book of which the third edition is still in print, and I believe that it had a significant influence in spreading an ecological interest in infectious disease amongst medical students and people more directly concerned with preventive medicine. It had some quite flattering reviews—though, fortunately rather late in the series, *Nature's* reviewer damned it as thoughtful but quite unreadable. I even had a letter from a literary agent in London suggesting that I write another book of popular science about every-day matters. Then I dredged up from somewhere what seemed to be the perfect title for the book I wanted to write—Dominant Mammal. Either way, one took the *double-entendre*: it said what I wanted to write about.

So most of my spare time in 1947 was spent in writing what came to be known by my family as DM. The idea of man as the dominant mammal of the earth whose whole behaviour tends to be dominated by his own desire for dominance gripped me.

It seemed to explain almost everything, and I applied it to everything. There could surely be no wider range of topics than those of my last eight chapters:

10 Industrial conflict and communism
11 Law and justice
12 The pleasant sins
13 Craftsmanship, science and art
14 Affection and cruelty
15 Values and religion
16 Ruling-class behaviour
17 The seven ecological traps

It all sounds incredibly naïve, but I do not think it was as bad as it sounds. There *were* interesting ways of looking at all those topics from the point of view of human evolution. And, in 1947, very few of them had been so looked at. I found it a rather exhilarating voyage of discovery and, undoubtedly, I learnt a great deal from the experience. Of the things I wanted to write about, only one foiled me completely—laughter. I tried twice, but nothing would come of it and there is no chapter on laughter in the manuscript.

I took DM seriously, had it typed in triplicate, and sent off the first copy to Curtis Brown. It was returned in very short time as not suitable for publication. This was a blow, but it was softened a good deal by an invitation from Penguin Books to do a Pelican on viruses. This eventually appeared as *Viruses and Man*, and again was well received and sold two editions. It was only natural that I should wonder whether Penguin Books would be interested in DM, so, having one foot in the door as it were, I persuaded their science editor, Mr J. L. Cramer, to look at the manuscript. He was interested, but told me (a) that the style was too ponderously academic, and (b) that when I wrote on sociological matters, I quite obviously made no attempt to bring my ideas into line with what contemporary anthropologists and social scientists were thinking and writing. Finally, I tried an Australian publisher and, after his refusal, I forgot it for twenty years.

On reading the manuscript again after those twenty years, much of it sounds rather trite and superficial, but very few ideas are expressed which I would positively disown today. For one reason or another, I have given more than my share of presidential addresses, memorial lectures, occasional addresses to graduating students, and the like. On turning over old manuscripts or reprints, it is very clear that most of the themes I have used appear either in embryo or fully-fledged in DM. I like to think that the world may have caught up with a number of the ideas. It is, perhaps, more likely that ideas that I had formulated when I was forty-eight or forty-nine are going to persist on into my seventies, irrespective of whether they are in line with what the world thinks or not.

In rewriting *Dominant Mammal* in 1969–70, I have used some of the material in the 'first edition', which I shall keep on referring to as DM, but in a different sequence and, I hope, brought reasonably up to date as far as factual matter is concerned. In many ways, it is less ambitious than before. I have not tried, this time, to cover the whole gamut of human experience in terms of dominance. It is, however, a convenient way to lead into the main theme if I give an outline of the earlier approach and try to assess, after twenty years, some of its virtues and weaknesses.

The basic theme was that, if we are to understand human behaviour and devise ways of dealing with social problems, the best starting-point is in the study of mammalian behaviour in Nature or in artificially contrived situations. Just as one can use principles of genetics worked out with bacteria or fruit-flies to help understand human inheritance, so can patterns of behaviour in mice or antelopes, baboons or chimpanzees, provide models which, used intelligently, throw light on human behaviour. The model situations are necessarily much simpler than human ones, and on account of that simplicity are available for critical scientific study. By comparison with different species, with due regard to evolutionary and ecological factors, it is possible, in the standard fashion of scientific work, to devise general descriptions, hypotheses and theories which may be appropriate for application to human situations. The justification of that approach is particularly clear in regard to the ecological position. One may study the relationship of man to his environment as human ecology, or discuss it in relation to demography or economics, but, from whatever angle, the same generalizations emerge:

1 Human populations were, and are, increasing at an accelerating rate, which will lead to chaos unless the increase can be slowed and eventually reversed until an acceptable and approximately stable level of world population is reached.

2 Planetary resources are limited, but technological progress is making it possible to squander the non-recurrent resources in a few hundred years—and the earth is likely to remain the only home of our species and its descendants for another 5,000 million years.

When we turn from ecology to the behavioural problems that beset us, it is still appropriate to look at what is emerging from ethology—which is the scientific study of animal behaviour—as the most promising source of useful ideas. In DM, I attempted to give a summary of the primary generalizations that emerge from the work of mammalian ethologists. A great deal more work has been done on animal behaviour since then, and I have browsed over enough of it to realize how conscious modern ethologists are of the complexity of the behaviour patterns they study in animals and how discreet they are in regard to generalization. With the certain knowledge that I shall suffer a sharp reprimand from any professional ethologist who may read this, I believe that there are still some valid generalizations about animal—and human—behaviour that I shall try to state briefly with a minimum of illustration.

1 The first imperative of life is to survive. Each individual animal must have access to air, to water, and to food appropriate to his kind. If that access is denied, there is an overwhelming drive to overcome the obstruction. It is equally important that the animal should avoid physical danger from accident and from the attacks of predators.

For fifteen minutes I once watched a solitary antelope, an impala that had come to drink at a pool in Kruger National Park. Yet, for the fifteen minutes we watched her, the impala did not drink. It was an illuminating and rather heart-rending illustration of the conflict between two inborn behaviour patterns, both necessary for survival. The doe was thirsty and she was at the edge of the water, but she acted as if she knew that to bring her head down to the water would render her wholly vulnerable to any lion or leopard that might be near. Each time her head moved toward the water the impulse to flee from a predator came into action and she drew back and looked quickly behind her.

2   Even more significant is the over-riding evolutionary importance of behaviour conducive to the survival of the species. In general, this coincides with the requirements for individual survival, but not always. There are many evolutionary adaptations associated with reproductive behaviour, courtship and mating, or parental care, which may prejudice individual survival while favouring that of the species.

Where display by the male is an essential preliminary to mating in birds, the elaborate decorative plumage of the male, as in the Argus pheasant or peacock, may be a positive hindrance to escape from predators. A different type of adaptation is the simultaneous birth of the young which occurs in any herd of game animals in Africa. The new-born are intensely vulnerable to attack by carnivores. Very many are killed as it is, but the numbers at the peak time are high enough for a sufficient proportion automatically to survive the day or two of greatest danger before they are fully capable of moving with the herd.

3   In all mammals which live in groups it is possible to recognize, more or less clearly, a ranking order amongst individuals, a hierarchy of dominance. Quite often there is one adult male who is the undisputed leader of the herd. In other species, the order may not be so clear or constant, but, in general, males can be placed in an order A, B, C, etc., such as that when A and B

together approach a single item of food, B will leave it to A, and when a decision on joint action by the herd is necessary, A will take it. In general, females are subordinate to males, but they can show ranking order amongst themselves.

4 Gregarious animals live in groups which differentiate themselves from other groups of the same species. Often, but not always, the group occupies a defined area of land, its 'territory'. The individuality of each group is manifested (a) by the fact that a member of the group, if separated, will seek actively to return to his group; (b) an individual of group B will be expelled if he tries to enter group A, and vice versa; (c) in territorial species, the range occupied will be defended against any other group of the same species.

Those broad principles of animal behaviour do not cover, in any way, the whole intricate range of patterns of action that we can see in birds and mammals, but they do provide a way of recognizing that, in a real sense, animal behaviour *is* relevant to human behaviour. In any professional study of behaviour in a given species it is always necessary to be very precise about the particular circumstances of the observations. Whenever an animal moves in search of food or in fleeing from an enemy his actual movements will depend on immediate circumstances; he will dodge a rock, leap over a stream, and so on. What is of special interest to us is whether the broad patterns of behaviour we have tabulated are instinctive, that is, are based on inborn qualities due in the last analysis to inherited configurations of nerve paths in the brain, or are learnt from parents and others. Without discussing the evidence, I think it can be accepted that in all there is a big instinctive component, but that in all animals, and pre-eminently in man, the inherited instinct (or more precisely, the genetically based nerve patterns in the brain) is better expressed as an inherited capacity to learn easily how to carry out behaviour to some particular end. A new-born antelope has full capacity to run with the herd and respond to danger. Man has to spend years learning to be a competent member of his group and his repertoire of behaviour is made far more flexible by his capacity for speech and for verbalized thought, which not only allows him to pass on information to another individual but also to transfer technical knowledge and cultural tradition from one generation to the next. Always, however, the human drive to action seems to be based on inherited behaviour patterns—or the nervous mechanisms which represent them—and these are clearly evolved from the same source as the behaviour patterns of other mammals. In particular, the principles of dominance and of group behaviour discussed under headings (3) and (4) are deeply concerned with all matters of human conflict.

I was well aware when writing DM that any attempt to discuss human behaviour 'as if human beings were animals' would provoke resentment in a large majority of unsophisticated people and, I suspect, from most people with scholarly training in any of the humanities or social sciences. Before dealing with those general objections it was desirable to make a more positive claim—to answer the question: Why do this sort of thing at all? The answer seemed to be obvious. Every man acts, in part, from the drives that have been enumerated, but also in accord with what he knows. He uses his intelligence according to how his inheritance and his education, in the broadest sense, have endowed him. Any man with social and political responsibility needs, in a real sense, to have some grasp of all knowledge. We are not concerned here with his specialized professional or technical knowledge, but with the necessary background knowledge of how things are done, of the differences amongst human beings and how such knowledge can influence the human approach that is appropriate to a given circumstance. He needs the ability to sort out the essentials of each problem as it arises, and either press for a particular solution forthwith or know how to consult intelligently the men or the books that can offer guidance for action. To provide a general pattern of understanding, plus a knowledge of how and where to find answers to detail, is the essential function of education at all levels. DM tried to show how the biological approach could be the basis of an effective education about human affairs.

There were two main groups of objections to be considered. The first is that any point of view which concerns itself only with things common to man and other animals must, of necessity, miss all that is characteristically human. It is far too facile to ascribe almost every significant human attitude to an elaboration of dominance-subordinance behaviour patterns. In particular, the characteristic contribution of Christianity, the humanitarianism, the sense of social obligation, which is visible in all Western writings on social structure, including this one, is left out of account. Goodness is not accounted for merely by talking about extension of parental behaviour patterns. We have to accept, it will be said, the absolute values of goodness, truth and beauty if the higher level activities of human beings are to be made intelligible. Even if we adopt a psychological-biological approach and interpret these values as reflections of some means toward survival, this type of argument must be based on the acceptance of some real value of the whole process of life and evolution.

The nature of values then becomes a matter which must be brought squarely into the pattern of this book.

The second group of objections will be those of the specialists; everyone who has extensive and scholarly knowledge of any field of learning or technique will find any simple approach totally inadequate. In DM, for instance, I had a little to say about possible origins of music and dance, but, later on, I tried to imagine how a scholar in the history of music would be likely to react to such presumption. Perhaps he might put his objection in the form which I quote from DM: 'An understanding of the history of music, of the technique of composition and execution, and of the styles and significance of the masters is a lifetime study. Without that study and experience of music, it is futile and pitiable to brush music aside in a dozen lines as a cascading elaboration of convention built up from the physiological rhythms of the dance and of vocalization. Similar objections can be raised from every other angle of human interest. Each aspect of the universe can be followed into an infinity of principle and detail and the only answer that can be made is that some aspects are simpler and more relevant than others.'

Throughout this discussion there were two conflicting principles which were always breaking in: On the one hand, there was the infinite array of complication, the detail, the unexplored tag-ends, the conflicting interpretations, which make the professional study of some aspect of the universe an endless fascination. In every subject, the professional student must always affect a real modesty of his own knowledge and a sharp contempt for the outsider who propounds preposterous generalizations in a field he does not understand. No one, we are assured, can nowadays take all knowledge for his field and get away with it.

But, on the other hand, there was the inescapable necessity that, on most occasions, decisions must be made on inadequate knowledge. Every human situation, every political situation is unique. The right course of action cannot be decided on precedent, because there is no full precedent, nor by scientific process, because science is concerned only with reproducible phenomena. Where, as is usual, there is a conflict of interests or opinions it may be sometimes possible to use the mathematical 'theory of games' to clarify the probabilities. Almost all decisions have, however, to be made rapidly without full knowledge of the relevant facts, and either at random or on the basis of a relatively simple set of principles the use of which has become a habit. The real objective of DM was, hopefully, to supply a simple set of principles that could be both acceptable and useful.

After DM had been laid aside in 1950, fragments of its philosophy tended to appear in anything I wrote, apart from strictly technical material. Here are a few examples of how the approach developed.

In 1952, I gave the Adelaide University Listerian Oration, under the title of 'The Seeds of Time: The Impact of Microbiology on Human Affairs Since Lister's Day'. For the most part, this was a survey of one hundred years of applied microbiology leading to the result that, even in 1952, it had 'made it possible for virtually every child born healthy to look forward to the normal span of life and in the process changed the whole biological structure of our species.' My peroration of that lecture gives, I think, a good summary of the significance of the human population problem:

'Perhaps I can draw together the threads of this Cassandra-like discourse by repeating what thoughtful biologists have been saying for many years—that man is a species of mammal that has arisen by the normal processes of evolution, and that he can survive only if he takes due regard of the processes that have brought him into being. His manipulative ability of hand and eye, his intelligence, language and his over-riding demand for power over his environment and over his fellows have led him progressively into a series of ecological traps.

'Urban life, a necessity for the development of civilization, inevitably led to the development of infectious disease. I have described how the science of applied microbiology has liberated us from that ecological trap but led us into the other of over-population. Birth control can save us from the evils of over-population, but confronts us with the new trap of genetic deterioration. Wherever we utilize knowledge for the short-term satisfaction of our desires for comfort, security or power, we are all too prone to find that, on the long-term view, we are creating one more ecological trap from which, sooner or later, we must extricate ourselves.'

As I grew older I began to be asked for addresses appropriate to formal occasions. Mostly they had a medical flavour, and a certain scepticism about the objectives of medical research and the effectiveness of medical care is a frequent characteristic of them. The years 1959 and 1960 were important to me for two reasons which have some relevance to my interest in human biology. On the one hand, I received the Copley Medal of the Royal Society and shared a Nobel Prize. It may sound like a crude and patronizing way to express my feelings, but, in a sense, those two awards placed me firmly at the top of the particular dominance hierarchy—status in the world of academic biological science—with which I identified myself. I think that this had an undoubted effect in allowing me to take a more objective, more liberated approach to the nature of dominance amongst men.

Also, in 1959 and 1960, I made my first visits behind the Iron Curtain to Czechoslovakia and the USSR. A scientist from the

West with good international standing probably finds it easier to admire aspects of communist society in action than any other type of visitor from the West. The scientists one meets are privileged people and the criteria of excellence in science are necessarily the same as in the West. I liked the sense of discipline and puritanism, the absence of advertisements or of evidence of 'conspicuous consumption', the unclogged streets. I had no wish whatever to live in Russia, but I could not escape from recognizing that the sort of future for human society that I had written about in DM might be more readily attained from a communist basis than from a liberal Anglo-Saxon-type democracy. But I was equally aware that if I were to write, as a Russian, the substance of DM, it would not only have failed to find publication, but its author would have been relegated to labour camp or insane asylum until he came to his senses.

Probably the next experience that was relevant to the eventual decision to rewrite DM was my meeting with Konrad Lorenz. Like thousands of others I had been delighted and enthralled by *King Solomon's Ring*, but I had, at first, only an inkling of Lorenz's significance for twentieth-century thought. By a happy and unlikely chain of circumstances, my wife and I spent a few days in 1963 as the Lorenz's guests at his Institute at Seewiesen in Southern Bavaria. This gave me a chance to appreciate the unique warmth of his personality and the depth and enthusiasm of his approach to ethology. Lorenz is a magnificent raconteur in English, which is fortunate as I have virtually no German. At that time, there had just arrived the page proofs of *Das Sogenannte Böse: Zur Naturgeschichte der Aggression*. We talked about it, but I had to wait three years before I could read it in English as *On Aggression*. Both the man and the book have influenced me greatly.

The final step toward rehabilitating DM probably came when I was invited to give a series of Boyer Lectures for the Australian Broadcasting Commission. These are intended to discuss matters of public interest in scholarly and understandable fashion. This, in fact, was the first occasion in which some major features of the DM philosophy were presented publicly. I called the series

Biology and the Appreciation of Life, and in the final lecture, Ethics of a Biologist, I tried to bring together most of the things I thought important.

Many of them had been foreshadowed in DM, but here they came out more clearly. At the same time, the lectures were written primarily and consciously for public delivery, with the hope that they would interest people and a determination to say what I felt had to be said without giving offence to anyone. I think that my main objective was, in addition to provoking an interest in biology for its own sake, to leave two ideas in the minds of those who might listen. The first was the way in which science could bring people from all countries together in a spirit of goodwill and, more broadly, that the task of bringing 'one world' into being must be the primary responsibility of an intellectual élite. The second was the desirability that in all tertiary education a suitably patterned course in human biology should be part of the first-year curriculum. Irrespective of whether a man is to be a scientist, a business executive, a professional man, a teacher, or in government service, he will be in a better position for knowing something of human biology. From another angle, it seemed to me that the only practicable way to inculcate something of the scientific approach in people wholly concerned with the humanities was to interest them in the scientific understanding of their own species.

When I retired in 1965 from professional scientific work, I decided that there were two main fields in which I should attempt to write. The first was to provide a theoretical interpretation of the immune processes in the light of ten years' progress since I had written about 'clonal selection'. The second was not so clearly formulated, but it had to be concerned in some way with human biology. Probably at the back of my mind the triple rejection of DM still rankled a little and I wanted to wipe out the indignity. The first half of the programme has been more or less accomplished with the publication of *Cellular Immunology* and its companion, *Self and Not-Self*, while another book, *Immunological Surveillance*, is in the press. The second half was delayed by the preparation of an autobiography, more scientific than personal, that was published in 1968 as *Changing Patterns*. A little, but not very much of DM crept into its final chapters.

In this second writing, then, I have a more limited but also, I think, a better-organized approach. As a reasonably intelligent man, retired from active life with a creditable record of achievement and no active ill-will toward anyone, I can claim to be, in one sense at least, above the battle. If, as a human biologist, I have an intense interest in the objective qualities of our species, and as a humane liberally minded man I am desperately alarmed at the current course of history, then it seems reasonable that I should try to weld those interests and to clarify for myself what sort of a world we should aim for and, given human nature as we know it, how we might move toward that aim. Hopefully, but not really seriously, I should like to influence the course of history to move, just a little, from the direction it will have if this book is never published.

The plan of the book, then, is something like this. First come what I call the exponential impossibilities, the processes now in action which must bring chaos if they go on as they are. This both presents the nature of the basic problem and implicitly states the only possible long-term objective, which I define as a stable human ecosystem for the earth. Then follows an attempt to present a highly generalized conspectus of human evolution and history in the biological terms which are now becoming relatively familiar to general readers. It is clear that, at whatever level one tries to analyse things as they are, there is more cause for pessimism than optimism about the prospects for a tolerable and indefinitely continuing world. Yet there are many things which are accepted as desirable by all intelligent people educated in any environment which has been influenced by Western-type thought, and the methods of science are accepted by all as a method of solving practical problems which at any particular time in history fall within their scope. The potentialities of science-based action are constantly widening. In the chapter on the ethics of a human biologist, I am primarily concerned with what can be universally accepted as good without regard either to the sex or temperament of the individual or to his involvement in religion or ideology or commitment to a particular national state—provided only that he is intelligent and able to think free of over-riding pressure from authority or from internal emotional disturbance.

To have a clearly defined ethic is not to ensure that behaviour will conform to it. Conflict arises between people and groups of people at every level of intensity and such conflict is inevitable in a species with man's evolutionary history, a species which has been forced to shoulder the burden of a world-wide civilization over a few thousand years with totally inadequate preparation. The key to the final chapters can be found in a sentence from *Biology and the Appreciation of Life*. There I said that the problem was 'how to use the intelligence of a relatively small number of men and women to devise ways by which patterns of behaviour laid down in a million years can be modified, tricked and twisted if necessary, to allow a tolerable human existence in a crowded world.' Any solutions must be *ad hoc* affairs adapted to time and circumstance, piecemeal amelioration of felt deprivation and resentment will always be essential, but if a long-term aim can be grafted on to world consciousness, then it may often be possible for the small scale necessary reform to represent a significant step toward the ultimate objective.

It is not easy to stand away from one's writing and assess whether what one is saying is both unequivocally intelligible and usefully relevant. At every point I am conscious of the difficulties of bringing anything that can legitimately be called a scientific approach to human affairs. Science, where it has been successful, has been concerned either with basically simple situations, like the dynamics of the solar system, or with *models* which it can devise and investigate in the laboratory. The molecular basis of life, the double helix of DNA and the machinery by which it brings the stuff of life into existence, was worked out, not on men or dogs, but on the most convenient laboratory model, pure cultures of bacteria and the viruses which can live on and destroy them. But the problems that worry us are the real problems of human actions taking place in what the computer men call real time. Questions become insistent.

Are the models from animal behaviour, the hierarchies of dominance, defence of territory, ritualization of behaviour, group cohesion, and so on, of any more value in understanding human behaviour than the conventional wisdom of politician, administrator or army officer? Does an understanding of the principles of animal ecology help in regard to the population explosion, the proper utilization of land and the problems of conservation? The whole book is an attempt to answer 'yes' to both those questions, but the real answer will have to wait on history. There are many similar writings being published and there is a clear indication that some people are interested. In Australia, the Australian Broadcasting Commission sold nearly 15,000 copies of my Boyer Lectures. Lorenz's *On Aggression* has been reviewed enthusiastically or with scathing criticism all round the world. I believe that this new approach to human affairs is working quietly in the same sort of way that Keynes' writings after the First World War gradually permeated into governmental economic policies everywhere in the Western world.

In a sense, it may be merely an attempt to implant a new mythology. Man is no longer something made in the image of God, but a part of the whole world of living things. Those aspects of human life that are common to all or most mammals may have to be expressed in terms which are so broad that they cannot be regarded as generalizations in the scientific sense. But those concepts are clearly more in line with the way people think in 1970 than the concepts of man's relation to the universe drawn from the Judaeo-Christian tradition, however much this may be modified nowadays by liberal theologians.

There is one final point which should be made before closing this chapter. In writing a book of this sort, a biologist will be liable to suggest occasionally means to an end which are currently unacceptable to large groups of people. This is something which has always been part of human history. In Bernard Shaw's words, 'biological necessities must be made respectable'. The process is visibly at work at the present time. The Pill has removed all taboos on the free discussion of birth control. Abortion is acceptable if there is a 25 per cent or more probability of a congenitally deformed child. In several countries, it is virtually the right of any women in early pregnancy who does not desire to bear the child to have a therapeutic abortion. Roman Catholic priests are claiming the right to marry and retain their priesthood. Other changes will become biologically desirable and physically practicable in future. It will be necessary to be sure that the changes are in line with long-term objectives acceptable to the community. If this is the case, concepts of behaviour that today are unthinkable to the conventional may, in due course, come to represent the ordinary attitude of Everyman.

two **EXPONENTIAL**
     IMPOSSIBILITIES

There is a current pastime, popular amongst the scientists, technologists and philosophers in American 'think-tanks', of predicting the state of things in the year 2000. The rules of the game are simple. One first looks at the changes that took place between 1938 and 1968. There are masses of quantitative data for almost everything that is of human interest: population figures, statistics of morbidity and mortality, changes in the gross national product, and all the lesser measures of economic activity in a thousand fields. The appropriate curves are drawn and extrapolated from 1968 to 2000. It can hardly ever be a simple continuation of a straight line. Almost every curve is an exponential one. When people talk of progress it is in terms of a percentage increase over the previous year. We do not express the cost of education in a country as rising at the rate of a hundred million dollars a year, but as doubling every five or seven years. World population doubles about every twenty-five to thirty years. All the curves move upward with accelerating speed.

The second rule is first to look at what was known at the laboratory level in 1938 and see what it had grown to at the practical and industrial level in 1968. Penicillin, television and artificial radio-active elements had just been discovered in 1938. The consequences for good and evil are there for all to see in 1970. Today we have, at the pre-commercial stage, new composite materials incorporating carbon fibres, fuel cells, techniques for deep ocean-floor exploration and drilling, hypersonic travel. All of these may have produced major industries by the year 2000. At the biological level, the only thing of comparable potential is the production of edible protein by micro-organismal growth in cheap and simple media derived from petroleum and atmospheric nitrogen. Despite much exuberant forecasting by men who should know better, I can see no application of biochemical manipulation of genetic material in even the distant future.

The rules have been widely applied, notably by Kahn and Wiener, and the results extensively publicized in the more high-brow types of mass media. World population will be over 6,000 million, an increasing proportion of which will be aiming at and achieving a standard of consumption equivalent to that of the United States today. Four countries, USA, Canada, Sweden and Japan, will have to be classed at a new level of hyper-affluent society. Giant urban conglomerates and innumerable highways will occupy a substantial proportion of the area of desirable regions of the earth. Most of the mineral deposits of current commercial grade will have been located and, in all probability, most of these will be under exploitation. There will be no major shortages yet, but one can foresee, in 2000, intense technological research on the utilization of low-grade sources of wanted materials. Metals from sea-water, fossil fuel from oil-shales, and more effective use of scrap-metal will all become increasingly important.

Perhaps the most important feature of the year 2000 will be the firm realization that exponential processes must come to a halt on a planet that must provide everything from its own resources, except for solar energy. Most of those who have written about the technical problems of the future have taken the view that, provided adequate supplies of energy are available, none of the impending shortages of fossil fuel and the rarer metals, such as tin, lead, zinc, nickel and copper, will be critical. Substitute materials can be provided from inexhaustible resources of aluminium, iron, magnesium, silicates and carbonates, with plastics from current vegetation, or from microbiological sources. This is probably true, but immense effort will be necessary before the new basis of technology is in full function. The first century of the third millennium AD is going to be a very difficult one for the captains of industry. But human civilization will go on through the third millennium and beyond, and our primary interest in this chapter is in defining the processes which must change their character of growth if we look more than twenty or thirty years ahead.

Of current human trends, those that are most important in determining the impossibility of indefinite extrapolation are:

1   In an affluent society most healthy women would like to have four healthy children. In poverty-stricken societies most have, like it or not, numerous children of which, nowadays, about four survive. Roughly, this means doubling every thirty years. The sequence, then, is for world population to double every thirty years to increase ten-fold in each century: 7,000 million in 2000; 70,000 million in 2100.

2   For the average person there is no limit to the goods and services that he can desire. The cost is far beyond the $3,000 per head per annum of the present USA.

3   De Tocqueville's diagnosis of America is true for the whole world: 'What the few have today, the many will demand tomorrow.'

Everyone is aware of the population explosion as an exponential process—which I have already defined as a 'compound interest'-type of process which can be measured by the number of years it takes to double in size or intensity.

World population doubling in about thirty years is simply the exponential process which has been most firmly impressed on world consciousness. No such processes can go on for ever, and it is obvious enough in relation to human population that the only alternatives are either to allow drastic depopulation through war and social break-down, or by deliberate action to control population by limiting family size to two children.

The second is clearly what must be aimed at if population is to be kept at a level which will allow a tolerable living standard to be provided from the renewable resources of the earth.

There are many other trends of essentially similar character.

The steady increase in CO2 content of the air from the combustion of fossil fuels with possible climatic effects—the clogging of roads with automobiles and the increasing death-toll from road accidents—increasing pollution of air and water—the rising deaths attributable to cigarette smoking—the inevitable extinction of all wild animals that become significant articles of commerce. Each of these trends is fully documented. Many of them can be brought together as manifestations of the momentum generated when science and technology are effectively applied to industry. The special quality of technological innovation, with its influence both on civil industry and on weapon development, is discussed later (Chapter Five).

In an entirely different area, we have the significance of education. As in all things, America leads the way. In 1930, 14 per cent of young people had tertiary education. Now it is nearly 50 per cent. This is not from a growing desire for knowledge, but from the simple realization that a college degree, and particularly a professional qualification, is a passport to relative affluence and security, to status within the community and to more interesting work which can be done very much at one's own pace. It means escape from physical labour or from routine time-clocked activities. Everyone wants what was the privilege of the few, and there is steady social pressure to lessen the requirements for entry.

The logical outcome will be a relatively sharp division of people into those over an IQ of 100 with tertiary education, and those under IQ 100 without. There is already the beginning here of a dichotomy that might be as pernicious as black and white skins in the United States. It will be an unstable and uninteresting world when there are no intelligent men farming, fishing, servicing motor cars, or running trade unions.

There have been many attempts to assess the growth of the human population of the world. It is simplest to assume that it remained almost constant for many centuries, rising almost imperceptibly from around 200 million in the days of Imperial Rome to about 500 million around 1650. The dates at which each successive 1,000 million was reached or will be reached are impressive:

1,000 m.	1830
2,000 m	1920
3,000 m	1961
4,000 m	1972
5,000 m	1981
6,000 m	1990
7,000 m	2000

If the population continues to double about each thirty years, as it is doing now, the figures for each successive century will be 2000, 7 billion; 2100, 70 billion; 2200, 700 billion; and so on. Obviously, something has gone fantastically wrong from anything Nature could have intended: the situation is becoming ecologically absurd. Yet the cause of it all is perfectly clear.

Nowadays, in Australia and most of the affluent countries of the West, we have a birth-rate around 20 per 1,000, a death-rate around 10, and a natural increase of 1 per cent per annum. In the Middle Ages, the birth-rate and death-rate probably both oscillated irregularly around 40 per 1,000. This, translated into human terms, means that the average family produced about five children born alive, with probably several other pregnancies terminated by miscarriage or stillbirth, and that more than half the children died, mostly from infectious disease, before they were adult. Until quite recently, this held also for most of the backward areas of the world. Let us remember, too, that, having regard to great differences both in fertility and in the causes of death, this is the 'natural' state of affairs for every species of animal in the wild.

Premature death in childhood has always been regarded by human beings as an intolerable burden—and everywhere in the world the success of medical science in preventing death in childhood is regarded as the most worthy of all human achievements. Those of us who have had something to do with the prevention of infectious disease take a special pride in that success. Only a hundred years ago the infantile mortality rate in the poorer areas of London was 300 per thousand. The best figures now are around 20 per 1,000 live births. Those 280 lives saved can be accounted for in all sorts of ways—education of women in mothercraft,

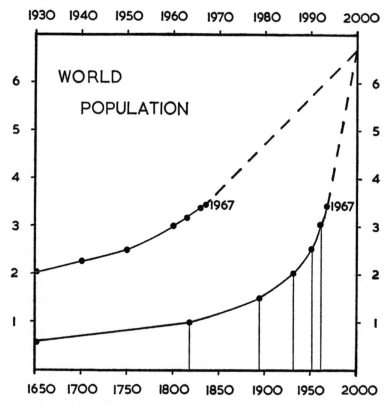

Fig. 1 World population and its extrapolation to the year 2000. Two time scales are shown, the upper in decades since 1930, and the lower in half-centuries since 1650. The vertical scale is in thousand millions and vertical lines show when each successive addition of 500 million was reached.

public sanitation, pasteurization of milk, vaccination, modern surgery, antibiotic drugs, decent housing. Everything that we cherish in a rising standard of living helps to reduce child mortality—but we must also remember that modern medical science can do a tremendous amount to save life in infancy and childhood *without* significantly raising general living standards.

I have often used the story of the elimination of malaria from

Mauritius as a vivid demonstration of this. Before the Second
World War, the birth-rate was around 33, with deaths about 27
per 1,000 per annum: there was a slow increase in population.
During the war period, the capacity of DDT to deal with mosquito larvae was discovered. A relatively-small heavily-malarious
island provided malariologists with a magnificent opportunity to
achieve complete elimination, and between 1946 and 1948 both
the important carriers of malaria, two *Anopheles* mosquitoes, were
exterminated. In 1952, the birth-rate had risen to 47, the death-rate
had fallen to 12. Deaths in the first year of life hovered around
150 before the war and came down to 60–70 in the 1950s. By 1965,
the birth-rate had fallen to 35.5, while the death-rate had gone
down to 8.6. In broad terms, before the elimination of malaria,
population increased about 0.5 per cent per annum, doubling each
150 years. After the malarial mosquitoes had gone, the population
of Mauritius increased from 420,000 in 1945 to 750,000 in 1965,
which is a rate approaching 3 per cent per annum. Mauritius is
a beautiful and highly fertile volcanic island, but its people have
only 720 square miles to support them and there is only one
exportable product, sugar.

On a bigger scale, the world is rather like Mauritius. It will not
be as easy to eliminate malaria from continental areas like India
or tropical Africa as it was from Mauritius, but everywhere rapid
progress is being made. The World Health Organization is already
proclaiming as a practicable objective the eradication of malaria
from the world. There is a hint that, as is the case of yellow
fever, there may be an alternative host for the malarial parasite
in some species of monkey in South-East Asia, and possibly elsewhere. This may slow the process of eliminating malaria, mainly
by making it necessary to maintain control measures much longer
than if man—which, in fact, means essentially, children—was the
only host. Given some success in maintaining peace, damping
down the population explosion a little and increasing the capital
available to poor tropical countries, malaria will have almost gone
by 2000. There are other causes of unnecessary death from infectious disease in under-developed regions, but for these, too,
methods of prevention are known. In brief, there is now no serious

MAURITIUS

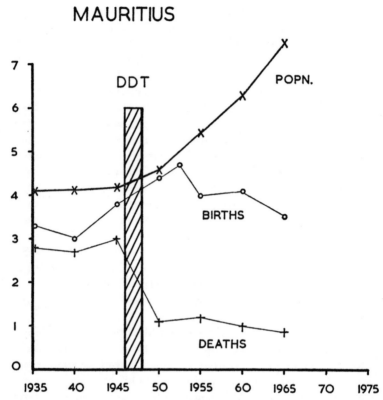

Fig. 2 The influence of malaria eradication on the demography of Mauritius. The bar marks the period when *Anopheles gambiense* and *A. funestus* were eliminated. Population in hundred thousands. Birth- and death-rates per 100 per annum.

impediment why every area on the globe should not reach the level of health now characteristic of Australia and New Zealand. Every country can look forward to the day when life expectation at birth is sixty to seventy years.

It will not be done until standards of living rise sufficiently in the poor countries to provide something more than vaccines, antibiotics and malaria control. The biggest obstacle to prosperity is over-population itself and, with the present great excess of young people in all the developing countries, a desperate effort will be needed to bring the birth-rate down to replacement level. If we omit all actuarial refinements, a population with an expectation of life at birth of seventy years would be at equilibrium with a birth-rate of 14 per 1,000, and a similar death-rate. Refinements and qualifications will be necessary, but a birth-rate of 15 can be regarded as an appropriate target for all countries. In only one, Japan, has deliberate action been successful in bringing the rate down significantly from 34 in 1947, to 17 in 1960. In neither India, Africa nor Latin America has there been any significant inhibition of births to counter the falling death-rates.

Possibly the most interesting of the exponential impossibilities concerns the present major source of energy for industrial use— the fossil fuels, coal, oil, oil-shales and natural gas. Extrapolation of current rates, having regard to a probable progressive increase in the demand per person for energy and the increasing population, indicates that the reserves of fossil fuels will be exhausted in about a thousand years. Concomitantly, there will also disappear, at the same time, the most versatile and convenient of the raw materials on which organic chemical industry can be built.

The fossil fuels were laid down over geological periods from the Carboniferous to the Cretaceous for the most part 130 to 350 million years ago. Probably a similar process is going on today on a relatively small scale where peat bogs are growing, or hydrocarbons forming at the bottom of the Black Sea, but there is no gainsaying the brutal fact that what took 200–300 million years to produce is being squandered in three or four centuries. If current astronomical teaching is correct, it could be that man and his descendants will still have some thousands of million years in which the earth—in the absence of large-scale human interference—will remain physically suitable for life, but without the fossil fuels on which our current civilization is based. There are more subtle and, perhaps, more far-reaching effects of the plunder and oxidation of fixed carbon in the earth, but they can be deferred for a few pages.

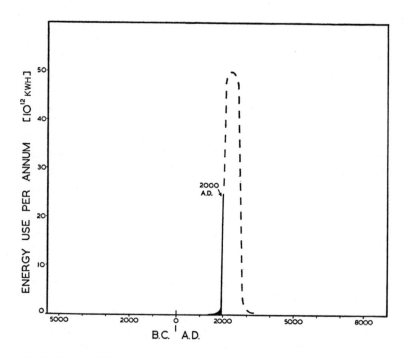

Fig. 3 The world's consumption of fossil fuel, past, present and projected, in terms of kilowatt hours x 10^{12} per annum. An estimate by an American committee on natural resources.

The only 'legitimate' source of energy for the world's uses is what reaches it from the sun and which can be utilized in the form of wind- and water-power, both, in the last analysis, generated by the heat engine of the tropical seas and from carbon currently being fixed by photosynthesis on the land and in the upper layers of the sea. Even with much more complete and systematic exploitation of sun-based energy by available methods the yield would be far below contemporary, let alone future requirements.

The successor to the fossil fuels has already established its position and in 1969 there is unprecedented activity in nuclear-plant construction, particularly in America. The new plants are designed to produce electricity as cheaply or cheaper than can be obtained from the best type of coal or oil-burning installation. After a lean period, the demand for uranium has quickened and uranium mining company shares are booming. There is a reasonable certainty that reserves of what are currently 'economic' uranium ores will soon be exhausted, but if the cost of extraction is not important, there are very large absolute amounts, though very low percentages, in granites in various parts of the world and even in sea-water. The enthusiasts for nuclear power look forward to new potentialities, the breeder reactors which, in stages, can use the whole of the uranium as fuel, instead of only the fissionable isotope, and still outside the bounds of current technology there is the possibility of controlled hydrogen fusion as a much more potent and potentially inexhaustible source of power to replace other sources of energy in the more distant but still foreseeable future. All these forms of nuclear power are illegitimate in any sense that has meaning to a biologist. Nuclear reactions are appropriate in the depths of a star, even more powerful sources of energy may play a part in the genesis of galaxies, but they have no place in a habitation of life. Evolution has only been possible since a blanket of gas developed around the earth to shield it from lethal radiations from the sun and from the other cosmic furnaces.

Nuclear technology was developed solely for war, and even optimists can only hope against hope that its use in war will not lead to the utter destruction of civilization and even of man himself and most other living species. A progressive never-ending expansion of nuclear technology to provide more and more extravagant amounts of energy may be almost as great an evil in the long run. Pollution of air, water and the environment generally is already occurring, and every radio-isotope is potentially dangerous. Most modern biochemical research makes free use of isotopically labelled compounds and every biochemist knows how easy it is to find his laboratory too 'hot' with isotope contamination to allow him to use sensitive counters in that room. Clinical diagnosis often makes use of similar labelled isotopes and 'hotter' ones have been used in therapy. The story that mortuary attendants

went on strike in a certain American hospital because of the
high level of radiation from the corpses is probably apocryphal,
but the mere fact that it was being told with a chuckle by people
with my own sort of background in itself tells a lot. The genetic
integrity of the human species is vulnerable enough from simple
demographic and social causes—it is biologically stupid to add
the specific genetic poison of radio-isotopes to the environment.
If Sternglass's thesis of the influence of minute amounts of radio-
active fall-out on the infant mortality of American children
should be confirmed, the need for the greatest possible care in
all industrial uses of radio-activity will be intensified.

The only recurrent source of energy that we have is that which
comes directly from the sun—it is also the only source which does
not necessarily pollute the environment. Current sources of solar
origin are limited to hydro-electric power and the use of wood
as fuel. If fossil fuels are to replaced by contemporary solar
energy, much more will be needed, and an American engineer,
P. E. Glaser, has recently suggested how it might be achieved. He
has the characteristic American attitude that what is physically
possible in principle can be made technologically possible, and if
it is needed for war, profit or human survival, it will be created.
He calculates that if solar energy collectors presenting a total
area of 1,000 square miles to the sun were placed in geostationary
orbit round the earth and the energy converted to a form which
could be beamed by micro-wave, the estimated energy requirements of the world in 2000 could be provided. This is far beyond
the means of current technology and, if it were achieved, any
mis-direction or wavering of those intense beams of energy on
their 23,000-mile journey to earth could be highly lethal. Nevertheless, the concept is important as being the only currently conceivable way by which a *recurrent* source of energy could provide
what an advanced technological civilization requires.

As things stand today, there is no biologically acceptable source
to provide for the world of the future the energy per person
which America, the paradigm of the future, demands today—
15,000 kilowatt-hours per year. Power supply is another of the
exponential impossibilities.

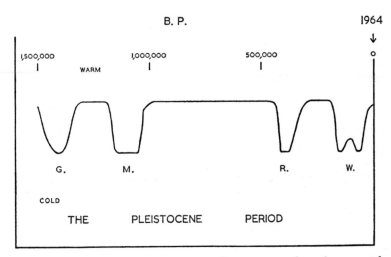

Fig. 4 Climatic change in the last 1.5 million years: to show the potential instability of the present. G, M, R and W represent the four glacial phases, while the plateaux of warmer climate show the inter-glacials.

Geologically speaking, the earth is just emerging from a glacial period. Only 12-20,000 years ago the level of the oceans was 200–400 feet below the present level, owing to the immense amount of water locked in the great ice sheets of the Northern Hemisphere and of Antarctica. At the peak of the last (Würm) glacial phase, 15,000 years ago, the maximal lowering to 130 metres (400 feet) exposed large areas of Continental Shelf and allowed human migration from the land mass of the Old World to the Americas and Australia. Over the past 1,500,000 years, there were four great ice ages with three major inter-glacial periods, the greatest more than half a million years in duration. There were also minor remissions during the glacial periods themselves. It is just not reasonable to believe that the earth has emerged completely from the ups and downs of the Pleistocene, particularly as there appears to be no acceptable theory of the basic cause of glacial ages or of the sequence of changes during the Pleistocene.

As a result, there has been much discussion as to whether

human activities may not trigger off climatic change in an intrinsically unstable situation, with disastrous results. The contingency most widely discussed has been the possibility of an increasing concentration of carbon dioxide in the air warming up the earth by the so-called 'greenhouse effect'. An increase in CO_2 could trap high temperature energy from the sun but diminish the radiation of low temperature energy into space. This could conceivably result in a melting of the Antarctic glaciers to give a rise in sea-level of something between 40 and 100 feet above the present, as it had been during some of the inter-glacial epochs. Every seaport in the world would be put out of action, and millions made homeless.

In the last three decades, there has been a general shrinking of glaciers and the sea-level is said to be rising about 2.5 inches a century. To reach 50 feet would require, at that rate, only the geologically trivial period of 25,000 years, but there would still be plenty of time for progressive re-siting of cities and ports as the water rose. The possibility of a more catastrophic result by which the Antarctic ice-cap slid over its melted base into the Southern Ocean has been suggested by Williams, and others.

Perhaps it is a little reassuring to find that another group of geo-physicists is almost equally concerned with the potential danger of an increased concentration of particulate matter in the atmosphere. An important and increasing source is from the jet trails of high-flying aircraft, and there are many others. The effect is, however, to cool the earth's surface by reflecting back some of the sun's energy into space. Neither the 'greenhouse' effect nor this cooling potential of particles in the atmosphere has become much more than a possibility for the future. Detailed information will need to be collected and analysed over another twenty or fifty years before any firm predictions of significant effects will be possible. But, if we are in an unstable climatic phase of an unfinished glacial period, there is much to be said for trying to maintain the *status quo*.

Even more fundamental environmental catastrophes have been hinted at. Oxygen is a highly reactive gas that must be constantly regenerated by photosynthesis in green plants, including particularly the algal phytoplankton of the sea. Deserts without green plants have been spreading in all the more arid areas of the earth throughout most of human history. The contribution of irrigation in modern times has probably been trivial in comparison. In the heavily populated parts of the world the displacement of vegetation by buildings, roadways, parking areas, and the like, is going on to a significant extent. Gross air pollution, for example, with sulphur compounds, can destroy vegetation, and one of the potential dangers of over-industrialization and unwise use of radio-active material is that the carbon-fixing oxygen-releasing organisms of the phytoplankton of the sea might be poisoned and the equilibrium destroyed. No one, as far as I am aware, has tried to assess the effect of full-scale atomic and chemical war on the essential—non-human—components of the earth's biosphere.

There is another aspect of environmental pollution which, although it threatens no drastic change in the environment, offers a curiously ambiguous type of danger. This might be called the menace of the unbiological chemicals. There is an almost unlimited number of organic chemical structures in the substance of plants and animals. Some of them are poisonous to other organisms, usually for good evolutionary reasons, snake venom or the atropine from deadly nightshade for example. But there is one thing all living substance has in common. Let it rot on the earth or in water and, in due course, the living scavengers, mostly bacteria, will break everything down to harmless simple molecules, nitrogen, water, carbon dioxide, sulphates, and so on, plus the complex substances that make the necessary humus of a fertile soil. We have all evolved together, animal, plant and microorganism, and we are all part of the cycle of life.

The organic chemist can make many substances that have no place in Nature. Like DDT and polyethylene, they have uses which seem to offer enormous benefits of one sort or another, but they have one terrible disadvantage. They are insusceptible to break down by bacteria, they are never:

> . . . rotted to flowers and fruit
> Like Adam and all mankind.

They litter the surface or the substance of land and sea, or, like DDT, can pass intact along all the food-chains of the earth. Even Antarctic penguins have DDT in their livers, and so have we all.

There are thousands of new chemicals for which commercial use is found each year; many are drugs or food-additives, many more will be taken into somebody's body by accident. Where men working with these chemicals are heavily exposed, dangerous mishaps, dermatitis, paralysis, cancer, can occur. When these are detected, government departments of industrial health make their studies and issue their safety instructions. The workers stay healthy and the factory continues producing the chemical.

Despite all that has been written about the dangers of DDT and similar insecticides which are present in every food from mothers' milk to deep-sea fish, I know of no evidence that the 'ordinary' amounts of a few parts per million have ever had any medically significant effect on anyone. This is where the ambiguity comes in. How do we know that it is not producing relatively large numbers of cases of stomach cancer anywhere from ten to thirty years after being taken into the body? Actually, in most parts of the world, cancer of the stomach is becoming rather strikingly *less* frequent, for reasons quite unknown, over the last twenty years. But how do we know that the fall might not have been much greater if it had not been for the DDT in the environment? This is an imaginary example of the unanswerable questions that are keeping public-health administrators unhappy. In October 1969, cyclamate, the favourite sweetener for low-calorie drinks and sweets, was banned on suspicion of being capable of producing cancer in man because some rats given large amounts developed cancer of the bladder. I don't believe that anyone thinks it likely that cyclamate will accelerate the appearance of cancer in human beings, but we must play safe. In parenthesis, we do not play safe about the most important extrinsic cause of cancer, which is cigarette smoking. That, however, is not only an accepted social habit but a major contribution to government funds in every country.

The point to be emphasized is our ignorance about the long-term effect of small amounts of 'non-biological' chemicals. Any one of them could conceivably be a potent but long-delayed stimulant to malignant disease in man. That fear is not unreasonable. In a technical book on cancer, at present in course of publication, I tried to work out what were the common factors of the chemical substances which are known to cause cancer when administered to rats or mice. The summary is, I think, worth quoting despite its use of a few technical terms:

'I believe that the only useful way to look at the mechanism of chemical carcinogenesis is to forget about all chemical detail and consider the situation as essentially an evolutionary phenomenon. There is virtually only one thing in common amongst all the ways in which cancer can be experimentally provoked in animals or clearly demonstrated to result from environmental factors in man. None of the substances concerned would ever have been encountered, except in some fantastically unlikely circumstances, during the whole course of pre-human evolution. The first chemical carcinogens came only with the use of fire for domestic purposes. Since then we have first slowly, and in the twentieth century at precipitous speed, built a civilization on unbiological materials, that is, materials that the mammalian body has not been adapted by evolution to handle.

'Any reactive chemical molecule which, because of the absence of enzymes to deal with it, or for any other reason, can reach the nucleus of a cell in significant concentration is liable to damage the genetic structures in random fashion. The type and extent of the damage will depend on the nature of the chemical, but having regard to the complexity of information in the genome and its expression in patterns of a relatively simple chemical code, it will still be random. Amongst the minor effects which still leave the cell viable there will be a proportion which affects those functions which are relevant to the control of proliferation and of intercellular relationships, and cancer results.'

It is hardly necessary to discuss all-out nuclear war as an exponential impossibility. Biologically speaking, it represents the final absurdity of human behaviour. Whether or not it will eventuate depends, or seems to depend, on the same sort of calculus which determines why an alpha particle emerged from a certain radium atom five minutes ago when the only rule that governs the event is that there is a 50 per cent chance of it happening in 1,620 years. Some have guessed that it may be close to the truth that there is about a 1:10 chance per decade that the bombs will be loosed.

The threat of nuclear war is the over-riding consideration of the present decade. If it comes, the book of Western-type scientific civilization closes for ever, and it is wholly possible that the human species will be finally destroyed in the aftermath of genetic damage to all survivors. There is much more to be said about what led up to the making and use of the atomic bomb in later pages. Here it is only expedient to say something of the alternatives which, if we did not have the nuclear bombs, could also have raised warfare to genocidal intensity. When scientific knowledge becomes virtually complete, war becomes biologically inadmissible. The story of Hiroshima, and what followed, exemplifies the final application of the physical sciences to destruction of life and everything that men have made. The biological sciences must be used in subtler fashion, but they have almost equal potential for evil. In the ABC of modern war—atomic, biological, chemical— the second and third have arisen mainly from the findings of medical research.

Chemical warfare, the use of poisons to kill or incapacitate human beings or to destroy crops or domestic animals, can be looked at first. As our concern is wholly with human biology, we can forget about defoliants and herbicides. Of the poisons available, the nerve gases are the most potent killers and their origin the most illuminating. In the 1930s, there was great interest in the research laboratories concerned with nerve physiology in the process by which one nerve influenced another, how the nerve impulse and the information it carried was ferried across the tiny physical gap, the synapse between the fibres of two nerve cells. Some thought the mechanism was a purely electrical one, others favoured some chemical process. The latter were eventually proved right. It is now known that the transfer of information from sense organ to brain and muscle demands an elaborate mechanism at the junction point between processes of any two nerve cells involved. An enzyme cholinesterase must function if the message is to be transmitted. Some drugs were known to be poisonous because they damaged that enzyme; they were anti-cholinesterases. Using the skills of the organic chemist to synthesize many variants of such drugs and experimental pharmacologists to test them for capacity to reach and damage cholinesterase in the nerve endings, Hitler's scientists produced the 'nerve gases'. These are chemicals, oily liquids, which have quite complex effects on nerve function, but, from the human angle, their only significant feature is that a drop or two lodging on the skin or inhaled leads to death within a few minutes. More lethal ones have been produced since, as well as a variety of less lethal harassing agents for riot control, and the like.

A rather different approach toward the same homicidal objective has been the elaboration of microbiology into fields far beyond the needs of preventive and curative medicine. Microbial genetics has already produced strains of bacteria that can resist all the common antibiotics so that they would be most 'useful' in biological warfare. Probably it is a point of view which can be easily overplayed, but it is inescapable that the more that is known about biological function, the more readily can that knowledge be used to help devise unnatural ways of damaging that function. If there had been no hydrogen bombs, equally potent weapons would be available for mass use, lethal chemicals like the nerve gases and the modern derivatives of mustard gas, disabling psychotropic chemicals based on LSD, lethal aerosols of antibiotic-resistant anthrax bacilli and, no doubt, a few surprises like a highly paralytic polio virus with a new antigenic character. In a sense, to mention these horrific possibilities is only make-believe; while the megaton bombs exist, the more subtle ways of mass killing will be kept in the background. What I want to emphasize is that virtually all aspects of science which are applicable to human affairs are known in principle and, given a strong enough motive, can be moulded into practical, large-scale application for good or evil—but more easily for evil.

I hold that it is beneath the dignity of science and scientists that the knowledge that has been won should be used for evil purposes, and the one unequivocally evil purpose is the killing, mutilating or rendering insane of large numbers of one's own species. War is a biological absurdity, an anachronism. It must be banished, yet there seems to be not one practicable suggestion as to how war can be prevented. For a period, it seemed that a balance of terror, deterrence by the threat of mutual overkill was the answer. Vietnam shows that it is not.

The modern methods of making war have not yet been used. Even the men who control them know that the exponential impossibility has already been reached in weaponry.

In this chapter I have tried to set the stage by propounding the 'exponential impossibilities' of our human situation. There are five great human problems which, primarily by the advance of science and technology, come into this category. Others may yet emerge, but for the present they are:

1 Over-population
2 Exhaustion of planetary resources
3 Pollution of the environment by radio-active and other un-biological materials
4 The threat of major climatic change
5 Modern weapons of war

Every one of these problems, in a real sense, has run away from control, and unless all of them can be controlled, chaos must result. The present time is unique in all human history, primarily, perhaps, because human history has been based on the progressive evolution of weapons and of the techniques of using them, and when weapons become absolute, then, to borrow a phrase from Gabor, history must have a stop. Neither scientists in general, nor human biologists in particular, are popular with politicians or the captains of industry, or, for the matter of that, with trade-union leaders or with generals, admirals or air-marshals. But, somehow, every man with power and responsibility must be made to understand how the menaces which hang over us—and they all more or less clearly realize these menaces—have come into being. This, I think, can be told clearly enough, but it is another matter when one tries to sketch out possible answers.

There may be no adequate answers. H. G. Wells, in his younger days, saw science as a builder of sophisticated Utopias, but died with a sense of complete hopelessness—man as individual and species was at the end of his tether. Things are worse now, and hedonism and existentialism has replaced the early Wellsian optimism. Perhaps only a biologist could dare to hope that there may be a sane and practicable way of ensuring the survival of our species.

DOMINANCE
three IN ANIMALS
AND MAN

The human situation in the late-twentieth century is beset with problems. Some can in practice, more can in principle, be solved by the application of experience, common sense and science. The one problem which has become almost progressively worse over the whole of history has been human conflict in the sense of antagonism, capable of developing to violence and homicide, between individuals or human groups. Very early in human pre-history, war, organized homicide between groups, became an essential part of culture almost everywhere and has ever since been the major force in shaping history. War, of course, is only the most conspicuous form of human conflict. In one form or another, conflict exists at every level, and it is a mere truism to say that if we got rid of the major manifestations of human con-flict there are no other problems which could not be solved.

There is obviously no simple answer, but it is still legitimate, as in 1947, to say that an acceptable scholarly interpretation of the basis of human conflict is the most urgent first step in the elimi-nation of war. The first step, of course, would in itself be com-pletely inadequate. It by no means follows that if the reasons for conflict were clearly understood by all who were in a position to influence social and political activities, war and criminal homi-cide, strikes and religious persecution could thereby be steadily reduced and eventually eliminated.

It did, however, give me a curious little surge of optimism to find that in 1947 I had written at this point in the argument: 'Even in the field of infectious disease there is one important disease, infantile paralysis, about which we know almost everything that is relevant to its mode of spread through the community, yet we still find ourselves completely unable to modify or prevent that spread.' Even while I was writing that, John Enders was starting the cultures of polio virus that in five or six years led to the Salk vaccine and the most effective elimination of a major disease in the history of medicine.

There is, of course, no real resemblance between the two problems. As a biological scientist, however, I must believe that the first essential is to comprehend the human qualities that are basic to all types of antagonism between groups and its extension to lethal combat. In terms of our biological approach, the problem becomes one of deciding (a) whether group cohesion and antagonism to other groups in man is basically analogous to what is observed in other gregarious mammals; and (b) how human conflict, almost alone amongst mammalian intraspecific fighting, is often to the death.

In Chapter One, I discussed some broad aspects of behaviour which could be taken as common to man and many other mammals. They covered the needs for simple survival and the behaviour associated with reproduction, involving, in addition to the physiological functions of impregnation, pregnancy and birth, the preliminaries of courtship and the aftermath of parental care and affection. The remaining aspects were concerned with interactions between members of the same species, apart from those concerned with reproduction, as shown by the emergence and maintenance of a hierarchy of dominance and the formation of groups with characteristic cohesion and exclusion of outsiders. It is with these two broad patterns of behaviour that we are necessarily concerned in this chapter and the next. In fact, from the point of view of the large-scale difficulties which confront us, these are almost the only categories of behaviour that are relevant. It is characteristic of our times that most people in peace-time enjoy their home life. There are exceptions, but, in general, people can develop a satisfying sex and family life, and for most people the circle of family, relatives and a few friends becomes their main interest and their refuge from the difficulties outside. In conformity with the title I have given this book, therefore, I shall forego any direct discussion of matters concerned with sexual and parental relationships or with affection in general.

To lead into some examples of dominance behaviour in animal groups, it should first be noted that there are two approaches to these matters. The ethologist is primarily concerned with the behaviour of animals as individuals or as groups in their natural environment, though he will also, on occasion, alter the environment deliberately to aid him in understanding. The second approach is that of the comparative psychologist whose interest is to devise experimental situations by which the various factors concerned in producing a particular type of behaviour can be analysed. Such methods can be applied to any available species, but, for obvious reasons, most of the work has been done with small or medium-sized animals and birds that are readily obtainable. Rats and mice, chickens and pigeons, have been the favourite species for such work.

Whenever two animals of the same species and sex are forced to live in association, a conflict situation will develop. Classical work on conflict has been done using each of the four species I have mentioned. The field was opened, however, by Schjelderup–Ebbe when he described the pecking-order of chickens and, in many ways, the pattern of behaviour in the barnyard offers the best introduction to the nature of dominance. It has the additional advantage that those of us who are over fifty will often have early memories of chickens in the backyard to substantiate what they read about. It is a pity that, since chicken-raising became big business, children no longer have this opportunity. To start with, then, we may take as a model of the process a group of hens.

Soon after the group is constituted, a social structure emerges, which is usually called the peck-order. If there are ten hens, there will be one who dominates the group; if she approaches a piece of food at the same time as any other hen, she will peck the other hen, who will then give way to her. A hen halfway down the peck-order will give way to four or five superiors, but takes precedence over those beneath her. Occasionally, there are small discrepancies in the regularity of the linear order, but this can be taken as the general rule.

In this set-up the sexual factor is excluded. With this limitation, we can say that the characteristics of the group are:

(a) The hens obviously identify themselves as a group in the sense that if one is separated from the rest, by a wire-netting fence for instance, she tries hard to rejoin them. It is equally relevant that a strange hen introduced into the group will be driven off.

(b) When the group is first brought together there will be competition for food, perching-places, and so on, which will produce minor pecks or quite serious fighting until the peck-order is sorted out and each fowl 'knows her place'.

(c) Once the peck-order is established, harmony is maintained with no more than ritual pecks. It breaks down only under rather intense provocation, for example, when only a limited supply of food is provided after a day or two's starvation.

When male birds are introduced into the flock, the cock dominates any hen so absolutely that he usually needs to make no display of his superiority by pecking. Amongst a group of males in a large flock of hens there is the same development of a superiority-inferiority order, which is then maintained with a relatively small amount of serious conflict.

To complete the picture, we must include the characteristic behaviour pattern of the hen and her chicks. The hen is, of course, completely dominant; if the chicks are to survive they must keep together and run to the mother hen at her call. Also, they must learn the practical details of the responses imposed by their inborn patterns, by imitation of the mother hen. As they develop, independence of behaviour begins to appear, the chicks range much more widely and do not flock back so readily to the protection of the maternal wing. A dominance-order amongst the chicks themselves develops, and as they reach maturity the males discover, sooner or later, their intrinsic ability to dominate any female, including the one who mothered and dominated them.

A very important aspect of the relationship between two

individuals arises directly from the parent-offspring pattern which is common to almost all birds and mammals. While the offspring are almost wholly dependent on the parent hen, she 'bosses' them completely, but, on the other hand, displays a high degree of altruistic behaviour. The best food is found and presented to the chicks, and the hen will endeavour to protect her chicks against any apparent danger with a relative disregard for her own safety. It seems to be a general rule that only when dominance is absolute does altruistic behaviour become possible. Amongst the ten hens of an established peck-order, Number 1 will strongly resent attempts by Numbers 2, 3 or 4 to share food that she is eating, but will raise no objection to Number 10 eating from the same dish. I can still remember, from childhood, how often one saw a rooster of completely assured position within the flock scratch up a dainty morsel and call up a hen to enjoy it.

There are many interesting minor features of dominance in the fowlyard, some of which have their human counterparts. Removal of Number 1 hen, the 'despot' of the group, will be followed by a period of increased conflict amongst the remainder until a stabilized situation again develops.

When a single strange hen is introduced to the group, she goes at once to the bottom of the peck-order, a place she is likely to retain even if she had been of relatively high rank in her previous group. Aggressive hens, however, after a time will work their way upward. If two well-acquainted hens with a defined mutual status are introduced into a strange flock, the dominant one of the two will usually help her partner to rise in the new social environment. Only when they have both found their places in the flock does the normal competitive relation between the two return.

These patterns of behaviour within a group of hens are so relevant to human conditions that it seems worth-while to summarize them briefly:

(a) When, by any means, a number of hens are brought together, they soon take on group cohesion in the sense that a separated individual strives to return to the group and a stranger's attempt to enter is repulsed.

(b) Within the group a quasi-permanent dominance-order emerges which is maintained without serious conflict. This relation probably grows out of the hen-chick relationship and it is characteristic that when dominance is absolute, altruistic behaviour becomes possible.

The facts are well enough defined to allow systematic experiments on what actually determines the place a given hen will take in the peck-order. Superficially the answer is simple: position is gained by success in fighting. This, however, only pushes the problem a little further back. The fights are not to the death, neither hen exerts her full physiological potentiality to damage the other and the loser cries enough quite soon. The difference that gives a higher place in the peck-order seems to be concerned with something that can be called drive, vigour or interest, push or aggressiveness, and is not directly related to muscular strength or skill in fighting. There are three possible sources of this vigour. It may be an inborn genetic characteristic, it may be related to seasonal or other changes in the individual's physiological state or to the individual's past experience. Probably all three factors play a part. Some breeds of fowls are intrinsically more aggressive than others; a broody hen under the intense hormonal stimulation of that condition may raise herself several places in the peck-order, and if the experimenter gives a hen low in the order sufficient injections of male sex hormone to produce most of the male plumage characteristics, she will immediately and violently come to the top. Past experience of conflict undoubtedly has an effect that, in human terms, would be expressed as confidence or lack of confidence. The hen introduced into a strange flock takes a place beneath hens which she would easily dominate if they were brought as individual strangers into *her* flock.

An interesting example of the interaction of hormonal effects and experience is given by an American investigator. A hen at the bottom of the peck-order of her flock was given regular injections of male sex hormone. After four weeks' treatment she began to work her way up in the order. As a rebel she had to fight hard and persistently to do so, but by the seventh week she was at the top of the order. Then treatment was stopped and the hen lost the male characteristics of comb and temperament. When placed amongst strange hens she was again a meek individual, but within her own group she retained the dominant position.

There is now an extensive scientific literature on animal behaviour as influenced by dominance relationships amongst individuals of the same species—and some American authors have coined the name 'sociobiology' for this infant science. Before turning to human problems, it is worth while to pick out from the records brief accounts of some of the characteristics of other animal associations to see how far they resemble behaviour within a flock of hens.

Male mice tend to be pugnacious creatures, and whenever they are kept in a group a dominance-order will be established. Different breeds of mice differ characteristically in aggressiveness. In other words, there is a strong genetic component in the quality. Experience of success or failure in combat is also important, and I believe that an account by Allee of some experiments on superiority-inferiority status between individual mice gives a very illuminating picture of the interaction of genetic and experimental factors. He described three breeds of mice with aggressiveness as different as their colours. They were a black, highly belligerent strain B, a brownish strain of intermediate aggressiveness Br, and a pacific white strain W. Mouse W1, who dominated his own group, was put into a cage with a mouse of the B strain and suffered defeat in every encounter. After several severe defeats, he was returned to his own group where his loss of confidence kept him for some weeks at the bottom of the social scale.

Then there was Br 6, a mouse at the bottom of the order in his particular Br group, a very meek mouse indeed. The experimenter decided to try to build up his aggressiveness by providing him with a series of successes. So Br 6 was mated and a low-order male W mouse introduced. In the presence of the female, Br 6 gradually developed aggressiveness and found that with only low-level W's to fight he was invariably successful. He became definitely aggressive and would usually win a fight with a superior in his own group. Then the final test was arranged. He was confronted with B2, a high-ranking mouse of the aggressive black strain. The fight was accepted and B2 won, but Br 6 fought on until he had received mortal injuries. The story has a ludicrous resemblance to the skeleton of a film scenario.

In experimental studies, the immediate cause of conflict is usually competition for food, but, in Nature, sexual and territorial factors are probably more important. In many species, successful mating is achieved by only a small proportion of males, very often in relation to their capacity to occupy and hold a territory. The primary conflict in such cases is for the right to hold territory. Opportunity for mating is simply a concomitant of success. Another important feature of the interaction of conflict, rank and territory is its effect in spacing out individuals and groups over the area occupied by the species. A Scottish ecologist, Wynne-Edwards, who worked largely with grouse, has shown the evolutionary significance of such patterns of behaviour in regulating population density to what the region can support.

During the last twenty years, there has been a steadily increasing interest in animal behaviour and there are few of the more conspicuous birds and mammals which have not been closely studied in the wild. Studies of primate behaviour, both in captivity and in the wild, have become particularly popular. For every species there is a broad pattern of behaviour, modified for each individual according to age, sex, temperament and circumstance, with each response adjusted to deal with the special quality of the occasion. As far as individual dominance rank within the group is concerned, the picture is broadly what it is in the poultry yard. In any real situation, mating behaviour tends to be conspicuous, with seasonal effects based, presumably, on internal hormone levels and territorial factors playing a major role. Various aspects of one or other animal model will need to be called on later to help interpret human behaviour, but most of the fascinating detail of the ethological studies concerns responses that have evolved specifically for the species being studied.

It is clearly only too easy to over-simplify the models that are obtained from animal behaviour. When one browses through a modern text, such as Hinde's *Animal Behaviour*, written by a professional ethologist for other professionals, one's chief impression is of the complexity and uniqueness of each specific situation. In almost every one of his summaries, Hinde warns of the danger of generalization from even the best-studied examples. In his own special field of the behaviour of birds he stresses the complexity of, for instance, the courtship situation in which 'tendencies' or 'drives' to attack, to flee and to copulate, conflict with one another in both male and female. Much has been made of displacement activities where a bird, unable apparently to attack or to flee, starts some unrelated behaviour, such as preening or feeding. The most likely of several possible interpretations, according to Hinde, is simple 'disinhibition'. Preening or feeding are very common activities easily induced and immediately inhibited by any more biologically insistent tendency. But when two major tendencies, as it were, cancel each other out, the easily induced activity comes into play.

Territorial behaviour is classical for chaffinches and other songbirds in Spring and is, in part at least, determined by hormonal activity. In Autumn and Winter, fighting between males in feeding flocks may occur, but only when they come within a few inches of each other. In Spring, the male will occupy a territory of as much as an acre, proclaim his ownership with song and drive off any other male that infringes the boundary. Yet the difference between the two sorts of behaviour is not sharp: 'In wet weather the bird may fluctuate from territorial to flocking behaviour over a period of a few minutes: at one moment the male may be feeding quietly on his territory in the company of a dozen other individuals, tolerating them to a distance of a foot or two, while the next, he will fly up to a song-post and attack any bird within a hundred yards.' It is evident that the pattern of song-bird behaviour is closely fitted to the ecological requirements of the species.

Another interesting elaboration on the theme of territory and ranking comes from the domestic tom-cat, as studied by Leyhausen. Each tom takes charge of his own particular territory and within it will be recognized as dominant by any other cat. When, however, he travels further afield, when courting for

example, he will have to find his place in an absolute rank-order
by fighting any local rivals. Even if he is defeated, he has only
to return to his home ground to regain local dominance over the
tom-cat which is his master on neutral soil.

Again, the behaviour fits the special requirements in this case
of an animal which has never quite been domesticated. In much
the same way, human behaviour is immensely complicated by
specifically human considerations. Application of the animal
models must be confined to the basic responses, and the example
of the group of hens is as useful as any.

To introduce the approach at the human level, in 1947 I tried to
provide a general picture of human group behaviour using ideas
largely drawn from McDougall and Trotter. Some of the relevant
section can be quoted:

'One can start by taking a realistic unidealised look at the
group behaviour of any socially homogeneous group of normal
males, adolescent schoolboys, soldiers, wharf-labourers, in fact
any unselfconscious group not under observation by persons
regarded as outsiders. While it is functioning as a group, those
composing it will take on a definite pattern of structure and
behaviour. In the first place, one individual will be recognized
openly or implicitly as the leader, while the others will arrange
themselves in a loose order of dominance. The order is not rigid,
changing, but usually only slightly, according to the type of
group activity involved. Each member tends to personify the
group as a single individual, this personification becoming increasingly definite when the group as a whole is considered
in relation to individuals or groups who have or claim superiority over the "in-group". In discussions of this sort, it is convenient to use the standard convention of the psychologists that
"in-group" refers to the group with which the person under
consideration identifies himself, while the other groups with
which this one comes into relationship are known as "out-
groups".

'Secondly, membership of the group is normally cherished, exclusion producing serious mental discomfort and being regarded as the appropriate punishment for any disloyalty to the purposes of the group. As a natural corollary, there is a dislike of taking strangers into the group and, when this must be done, there is often an elaborate ceremonial of initiation, the main function of which is clearly to impress on the newcomer how inferior he is to established members of the group he is joining, and to show him that his place in the dominance-order is, for a start at least, at the bottom.

'Leadership in such unsophisticated groups is dependent on a complex of characters. The essentials seem to be:

(a) physical courage, especially in combat;
(b) heterosexual interest and competence; and
(c) enthusiasm in his identification of the group's aims with his own, particularly in regard to the group's hostility to other groups.'

This general pattern corresponds well to what was described by Homans in 1950 as characteristic of 'the human group'. Some of the main points he made from systematic observation of the same sort of relatively unsophisticated groups were (1) the higher an individual's rank, the more he talks and is talked to; (2) people are more likely to talk to others who are close in status to them; (3) conformity to group attitudes increases the popularity of an individual, and the closer he comes to realizing the norm of the group, the more likely he is to be regarded as leader.

Even at more sophisticated levels there are close similarities of group structure to these standard patterns. It is evident, for instance, that the person who will be the effectively dominant figure in a high-level administrative committee has qualities broadly similar to those seen in the leader of the schoolboy gang. Using the same headings, they are:

(a) effectiveness in discussion (verbal combat) which will include both drive and intelligence;

(b) prestige brought in from some other field: wealth, breeding; military, sporting or intellectual distinction; and
(c) enthusiastic identification of the group's interests with his own.

It is, in fact, impossible not to recognize the basic analogy of the dominance-orders in groups of hens, rats or mice, with those that form so broadly uniform a pattern in human societies. Most of the rest of this discussion will be occupied with tracing the implications of this generic resemblance.

Before trying to come to terms with dominance in man, how it is expressed and how it may have evolved, something more should be said about the concept of instinct in man. It is well known that a whole generation of anthropologists, educationists and social scientists took the view that instinct played no significant role in human behaviour beyond the more or less reflex activities of the new-born infant breathing, sucking, crying, etc. Under the influence largely of the ethologists, that outlook has changed along the lines I indicated in Chapter One. There are some further factors related to behaviour patterns in man to be discussed, and as background to that discussion I shall adopt a view that derives largely from Lorenz, Tinbergen and Washburn. It is certainly over-simplified, but it may be a useful simplification. On this view, those broad aspects of human behaviour that we can recognize as generally corresponding to that of mammals depend on a relatively small number of inborn patterns of easily learnt behaviour. When experience shows that one type of behaviour is very much more easily learnt than some alternative, it is justifiable to use the word 'instinctive' for its basic quality. These instinctive reactions must involve genetically determined qualities of the nervous system, but there is nothing really known of the qualities at the neurological level. Characteristic human examples that can be mentioned without discussion at present are speech, the use of tools and weapons, and reproductively significant behaviour appropriate to the sex of the individual.

These 'instincts' require three qualities to determine how they are expressed in action:

(a) intelligence;
(b) drive or aggressiveness; and
(c) pressure of the social environment.

Very broadly, it can be said that intelligence and muscular skills will determine the effectiveness of the behaviour, aggressiveness will determine its persistence against opposition, while social pressure will determine, in most cases, the objects toward which the behaviour is directed.

From the general standpoint that we are adopting, intelligence could be broadly defined as effectiveness in the use of tools to procure a desired object, including particularly that supreme human tool, the use of words, voiced or written to transmit ideas, or manipulated in thought to devise ways in which desires may be achieved. There is no question that human beings differ greatly in the effectiveness with which they accomplish set tasks. Intelligence tests merely provide a quantitative measure of the effectiveness with which certain tasks graded in difficulty are carried out. They all have limitations, the most important of which is that to succeed in any task calls for interest and drive, as well as the possession of the tools required. But, after making due allowance for all limitations, it has been fully established that there are wide quantitative differences in human intelligence and equally wide differences when any special muscular or mental skill is quantitatively examined. There is a general tendency for an individual who scores high in any test for ability also to show more than normal ability in any other type of test. This is no more than a general trend. It is very rare to find men with really exceptional gifts in more than one field. Men who in later life have been supremely gifted have almost always demonstrated their ability early in childhood and, subject to the inevitable difficulty of sorting out the influence of genetic inheritance from that of early upbringing, there is much to indicate that inheritance is a main factor in determining differences in ability, specific as well as general.

In this discussion, intelligence, to a large extent, can be left in the background. We are concerned with the direction and persistence of behaviour, rather than with the effectiveness with which it accomplishes its objective.

As I mentioned in Chapter One, I found when I was writing DM that I was recognizing dominance relationships in almost every type of human experience. It was so obviously important that I wondered why there was virtually no discussion of such relationships in any of the text-books and general writings on psychology that came my way. It was implicit in every intelligent novel I had read—later on, I was interested in looking at the action in *The Masters* and others of C. P. Snow's novels from this point of view—but academic psychologists seemed to leave it severely alone. I thought I could understand their reason for declining to deal at an academic level with so touchy a subject. There had been some useful work done by psychologists in assessing candidates for officer training in the Second World War for qualities of leadership. But this is a different matter from applying psychological tests to ministers of state, managing directors, army generals, and the like, or even to one's senior academic colleagues! I felt certain that if academic circumstances had allowed and a valid technical approach *had* been possible, we should probably now have standard tests for DQ (dominance quotient) broadly analogous to the IQ derived from the results of intelligence tests.

This is an idea which I have been playing with ever since. I think it will clarify my approach to spend a little time exploring the possibility of assessing a child's or an adult's DQ. Some children are clearly more aggressive than others and, in part, this must reflect genetic differences.I have not been able to find any account of a serious attempt to assess the genetic component in childhood aggression and submission. In view of the importance that has been claimed for the influence of human contacts in early infancy on subsequent temperament and behaviour, it might be very difficult to do this. The fact that identical twins are usually as alike in temperament as in physical appearance makes one confident that there *is* a genetic component, but it remains to be proved. However, it is largely immaterial what are the precise parts played by Nature and nurture in producing differences in aggressiveness. There is no doubt that such differences exist. At the crudest level, some children are bullies; some, and some only, are bullied. Perhaps it is to overstate the position somewhat, but on virtually every occasion where two human beings come into more than trivial contact, one of them is in command of the situation. Such dominance may, however, be very much dependent on circumstances. I can remember when I was a very young resident doctor on casualty duty ordering drunks with cut heads around with complete confidence, knowing very well that if I had been forced into association with any one of them under less clearly defined circumstances, I should have been acutely uncomfortable and very far from dominant!

In discussing superiority-inferiority relationships amongst people, one almost at once comes up against the same difficulties which give IQ results such a limited value. There are so many different ways by which mutual rank can be determined, just as there are such diverse sorts of achievement that can be evaluated in intelligence tests. I believe, however, that just as one can often be dogmatic in saying that X is very much more intelligent than Y, so one can also say, not infrequently, that P would dominate Q under almost any conceivable circumstance. The range of qualities which can give dominance, however, is very varied. In the more primitive situations, sheer toughness, with the capacity to threaten and exert violence, may be the determining factor. Much more often it will be a combination of capacity and confidence, plus the intangible element of charm, of being able to win people's affection, that brings leadership. In both circumstances, however, there must be a certain drive to achieve superiority that allows the individual to make the best use of those qualities he possesses.

Most human situations are more complex than any face-to-face choice of who is the better man. Every functional organization has a basically hierarchical structure of control, and its own rules and tradition for allocating people to the appropriate place in the ladder of authority, as well as for promoting, demoting or retiring them. Seniority plays a major part, but never a completely overriding one. The effective status endowed is greatly influenced by tradition. There is a very great change when a senator becomes the President of the United States, or even when a scientist becomes President of the Royal Society. At considerably lower levels, one might mention the rather special tradition of respect for status within the 'learned professions'. A physician, and even more a surgeon, must necessarily place himself in a position of almost complete dominance vis-à-vis his patient. In that relationship he must demand complete authority. This, perhaps, rubs off a little on to relationships within the profession. There is a very clear gradient of dignity from the consultant surgeon down to the medical student, and a correspondingly meticulous code of behaviour. The legal profession and the Church have a more formal structure of authority. In the academic world, the once God-like status of the professor has been diminishing rapidly, but he is still a significant figure.

It is clearly a gross over-simplification to say that men reach status basically in accord with the level of some DQ which, like IQ, has developed under the influence of both genetic and environmental factors. But other things being approximately equal, I believe it is the quality of drive, expressible as DQ, which decides who gets the chance to move up more rapidly. There is, however, one feature about place in the peck-order that is very different from intelligence. Whatever the route by which rank, status, prestige—dominance of any sort—is reached, it is something to be held or improved. It is always painful to be demoted. I have no doubt that the predominant cause of economic inflation is that only under quite exceptional circumstances can a man's wages or salary be reduced. It rises with seniority, and whenever it is readjusted to allow for cost of living, work-value, or anything else, it must always be upward. Inflation and taxation will see that the real value changes very little or even diminishes, but self-respect is retained.

Lorenz has an entertaining story of a little female jackdaw who was very low in the peck-order. Then one day, as a result of some complex mishap, a very high-ranking jackdaw lost his mate. He took up with the lowly female and, according to Lorenz, she forthwith moved swiftly up the peck-order and in a day or two was showing her superiority to upper-class female jackdaws who previously would have never even noticed her.

The patent biological necessity for the young to submit to the guidance and domination of their parents and, equally, when they become adult, to take over the guidance of their own immature offspring, makes it inevitable that in all mammalian behaviour there will a degree of ambiguity in dominance relationship between individuals. This is classically seen in the process of adolescence when it is desirable that the child should free himself from the domination of his parents. The struggles between the habit of submission and the urge to independence are obvious to everyone and usually painful to all concerned. The process is probably never complete. All men and women, at some time, desire to dominate their fellows, yet the great majority retain sufficient of the attitude of immaturity to find comfort in submission and loyalty to some person or to some personification of a human group or of an abstract ideal.

The social pressures which determine the direction of action nearly always spring from the individual's involvement as member of a group. A little preliminary discussion of the significance of the group, the herd or the crowd, to the individual is called for.

Without endeavouring to go more deeply than is expedient to a biologist, we must accept the central feature of human consciousness as it presents itself to the individual. Each of us, to himself, is something which persists, which is self-evidently the same from earliest memory until death. It is unanalysable; it is the ego on which the world impinges through the senses, which makes decisions for action, and which through the body—which sometimes seems indivisable from the ego and sometimes strangely other—acts in relation to the rest of the world. Persona is perhaps the best word to use for a man's complex mental image of himself as a perceiving, thinking, active unit.

To all men, primitive or sophisticated, it is the one unequivocal reality. And it is automatically accepted that every other human being has a similar unity, his own persona. It is easy to transfer a similar attitude to the behaviour of any animal considered as

an individual. In fact, it is probable that with the first development of verbalized thought beyond the immediate necessities of
living, primitive men tended to think of anything about which
they were constrained to think in a personified form. The personification of natural forces in the guise of gods is typical of all
the early mythologies, but far more important is the personification of a man's own in-group, especially in its relation to hostile
out-groups. The sense of belonging to a group must have been the
most real thing in a primitive man's consciousness of things
beyond his immediate sensations. It is inevitable that the group
should be spoken of as a person and that the man should feel that,
in some way, he and the group are identical. This is almost as
much a characteristic of modern man as of any primitive. Every
one of us has a whole series of groups of people with whom he
identifies himself to varying degrees. The groups may be large or
small, temporary groups coming together by chance and a range
of more permanent groupings up to race, nation or alliance. Such
identification with a given group is in no way incompatible, either
with the attitude that the group has a quasi-parental dominance
over him, or with endeavours on his part to exert the greatest
possible dominance over other members of his community.

Once the group has been personified, it will have conferred
on it the necessity of acting toward other personified groups in the
same sort of way as individuals behave toward one another within
the group. In other words, the most common interactions between
in- and out-groups will be felt by their component members as
essentially those of rivalry for domination, with something of the
character of their own urge for personal dominance.

One of the necessary approaches to understanding war and
human conflict in general is to be found in the universal compulsion of people to endow on any group of which they become
willing members a pseudo-personality basically similar to their
own. It is concerned, like the individual, to think and act for its
own advantage and to resent any obstruction by other competing
groups. It is readily moved to assert its superiority over out-groups
of similar function and status, or where the facts do not allow any
claim to present superiority, to try hard to rectify the situation in

future. At the same time, the group personality takes on the same ambiguity in regard to the dominance-subordinance relationship as marks that of the individual. Loyalty and submission to a dominant person or quasi-person is still possible to the group. A Waterside Union may quarrel violently with a Transport Union over the delimitation of the rights of their members to do this or that work, but they will co-operate enthusiastically in a general strike and, on the outbreak of a 'popular' war, throw in their lot whole-heartedly with the rest of the community.

Before closing this sketch of the role of dominance in human affairs, a little should be said about its bearing on religion, in particular on the idea of God. I find myself strongly sympathetic with the views expressed by Lynn White (1966) in discussing the historical roots of the ecological crisis. His attitude was that the scientific technological materialist approach—which is responsible for our exponential impossibilities—is traceable to the intensely anthropomorphic concept of God in the Judaeo-Christian religions from which our civilization has drawn its central concepts. In both Graeco-Roman and Oriental religions, animals, trees and rivers could have divine or spiritual significance, as well as humans. The Jewish monotheism quite unequivocally adopted an anthropomorphic God—with all the characteristics of a dominant male tribal chief. Christianity, still further, shifted religion to an exclusive concern with human beings by regarding Christ as a fusion of man and God. Christianity and the two Judaeo-Christian heresies, as White calls them, of Islam and Marxism are all wholly concerned with man, with interactions between men and with human attitudes toward a personified God, or its equivalent, and a human go-between—Christ, Mahomet or Marx. All three religions are dominated by a faith in perpetual human progress—and a basic lack of interest in the rest of the living world. The same holds, at least in part, for modern atheistic-humanist philosophies, such as the one to be outlined in my Chapter Seven on the ethics of a biologist. White concludes with the very interesting suggestion that, of the great Christian teachers, only St Francis of Assisi preached the virtue of humility not merely for the individual but for man as a species. There is the germ of a thought here as to how Christianity may develop if Western civilization survives.

THE EVOLUTION
four OF HUMAN
BEHAVIOUR

Anyone interested in human evolution will necessarily find that he must consider the evolution of behaviour at least as closely as the anatomical changes that have taken place during the few million years that are relevant. There are many basic needs common to all mammals, and almost anything that another mammalian species finds it necessary to do for survival will find some sort of an equivalent in human behaviour. The evolutionary processes by which those equivalents developed are legitimate objects of interest. A priori, one would imagine that both physical inheritance of brain structure and the development of behaviour by imitation and other forms of learning would play their parts, with the second becoming progressively more important. Quite early, it opened up an infinite range of actions and patterns of behaviour far beyond the capacity of any other animal.

In this book, however, I am concerned only with the broad mammalian trends as they are expressed and modified in man. Conflict, and the phenomena of rank, territory and war which grow out of it, provides the central theme, and to a very large extent this chapter is concerned with the evolution of conflict.

To most biologists, the two unique characters of *Homo sapiens*, which separate him from all other primates, are his capacity to speak and his habit of using weapons to kill other members of his own species. The evolution of speech is a matter of the greatest interest, but it is something of wholly different quality from behaviour associated with drives for food, sex or dominance. Speech is a tool to be used like any other tool. It is the print-out of a computer which, for all its complexity and competence, provides no intrinsic drive to action. As Fred Hoyle once said, the 'new' brain, the cerebral cortex, is of great size and can do immensely complex things, but it will only do them at the urging of the lower centres, 'peanut-sized brains' that we inherit little changed from early mammalian or even reptilian ancestors.

We are interested primarily in the origin of the drives that lead to conflict between men. We can speak of human instincts, provided we recognize that we are really speaking of inherited neural configurations which make it specially easy to learn the behaviour we ascribe to the instinct. Young men through the whole of history have found it easy and gratifying to learn how to use weapons skilfully, whether in killing animals for food or in combat with men of another group. This could be the stem from which the tradition of war, and the progressive elaboration of weapons and the strategy of their use, has become the core of human history.

There are still anthropologists who claim that there is no intrinsic drive to lethal combat in the human species. In their view, war, like the rest of human behaviour, is based on learned tradition and is in no sense instinctive. Instinctive human reactions, they say, tend as much to co-operation with others as to conflict. In a discussion of the problem of 'men's willingness to hurt and kill his fellows and take pride and pleasure in so doing', Geoffrey Gorer concludes that man has no 'killer' instinct, he merely lacks inhibitions. In support of this view, he cites three groups of primitive peoples, the Arapesh of New Guinea, the Lepchas of Sikkim and the Ituri pygmies of the Congo rain-forest, where men seem to find no pleasure in dominating or killing members of other groups and where there is no tradition of war. They are all small, technologically backward societies, living in inaccessible and, to their neighbours, undesirable environments. Gorer makes the interesting generalization that 'they all manifest enormous gusto for concrete physical pleasures, eating, drinking, sex and laughter . . . and they have no ideal of brave aggressive masculinity.'

The existence of such tribes may bring a ray of hope to the idealist and introvert, but it hardly counter-balances the evidence from the other 99.9 per cent of human societies. A geneticist would probably speculate that the 'gentle' peoples arose by 'drift', that is, each group was derived from a single family which happened to have this particular combination of genes; they survived only by retreating to inaccessible areas. This does not rule out wholly Gorer's contention that their gentleness is directly related to their tradition of shared sensual pleasures, and that warlike activity is associated with puritanism and excessive differentiation of male and female virtues.

Despite the views of Gorer, Montagu and others, the course of history, and the building up of human populations in the more fertile parts of the earth, has been the responsibility of the peoples who found it easy to use weapons and to kill those not identified as of their own group. It is an overstatement, but perhaps a justifiable one, to say that if we are interested in understanding current social and political conflicts in terms of the development of human behaviour there is only one area of primary interest. It is to understand the evolution of weapons and the instinctive, intellectual and technical developments of men and their cultures that followed and were part of that evolution.

Man, zoologically speaking, is a primate with many resemblances to chimpanzee and gorilla. All three must have had a common ancestor in the sense that, at some stage, there was a freely interbreeding population of earlier primates from whose descendants there eventually developed the populations of the three species that we know today.

General opinion amongst palaeontologists is that this ancestral population may have been ten to fifteen million years back in the Miocene. However, in the last ten years a new yardstick of evolutionary separation between species has been developed from the differences in structure of corresponding proteins. Human haemoglobin, for instance, is chemically very similar to an ape's, much less similar to that of a horse and remote from that of an earthworm. There are both quantitative measures of such differences and a reasonable genetic theory of their origin and frequency. In 1969, an examination of the various mammalian proteins that had been studied in this way indicated strongly that four to five million years was ample for the chimpanzee-gorilla-man divergence. The first unequivocally accepted member of the populations on the way to man is *Australopithecus* of South Africa and the related forms from India, East Africa and Egypt.

There are several localities in South Africa where relatively large numbers of fossilized remains of Australopithecines have been discovered, Dart and Broom being the men chiefly responsible. I once spent an evening with Raymond Dart in Johannesburg at which he produced an *Australopithecus* skull for me to handle. He talked, too, about the other bones found in these limestone deposits and of what he deduced from them of the 'ape-man's' way of life. As far as my reading goes, Dart's interpretation is still the one most widely accepted.

Australopithecus lived about 1½ million years ago at the end of the arid Pliocene period. His ancestors had come down from the trees as the African forests diminished in area over the preceding millions of years, and *Australopithecus* still had the teeth appropriate to an ape of the trees, living on fruit, nuts, insects, young birds, and the like. He had, however, become a ground-dweller, standing and running upright on two feet, with hands and arms freed from their former function of swinging the ape from tree to tree. If Dart is correct, *Australopithecus* had been forced, by circumstances, to become a carnivore feeding on relatively large animals, like antelopes. The other carnivores of Africa, the lion, the leopard or the hunting-dog, have evolved an anatomical equipment of teeth and claws specialized to capture and kill their prey. Along with these, they have developed appropriate patterns of hunting behaviour. The ape, come down to the ground, had to find some substitute for teeth and claws within a time far shorter than would be needed for their anatomical evolution. As the Australopithecines developed, such activities were elaborated. In their hunting, they probably used clubs from wood or the long bones of animals, primitive wooden spears and unworked stones for throwing. The tough skin of antelopes and larger animals would also need to be torn open by some primitive tool, a requirement that may well have led to the first deliberate attempts to produce sharp edges from chipped stone.

Chimpanzees probably live much like the forest ancestor of *Australopithecus*. Occasionally, they catch small mammals and eat them, and in a primitive fashion they make use of tools. A thin stick will be poked into a termite mound so that any termites on it when it is withdrawn can be licked off and eaten. Occasionally, crude attempts at using sticks or stones as missiles have been seen. Chimpanzees have, however, only a loose and amiable easy-going group structure. There are differences in rank, but no established leader of the group. Animals can move from membership of one group to another with a lot of noise but little ill-will, and serious fighting is either non-existent or very rare. Clearly, if this was the general pattern of the arboreal ancestors of the early hominids, there were many changes that had to be made in behaviour patterns when the trees were forsaken for the ground.

Perhaps the fount and origin of all man's misfortunes can be traced to the fact that he changed too rapidly from a browser on fruit and a snapper-up of trifles to a hunting carnivore. Everyone who has read Lorenz remembers his dictum that any species of carnivore which is capable of killing another of its own kind will develop rituals of surrender which automatically 'turn off' the attack of the victor. When wolves or dogs fight seriously, there comes a point when one gives up the fight by rolling on to his back and, as it were, presenting his most vulnerable areas of throat and belly as a gesture of submission. The winner could kill but never does; he allows the loser to run off tail between the legs, while *he* struts with a new sense of dominance.

No one will ever know the details of how *Australopithecus* became a hunter, and perhaps it will not even be possible to establish that he was ever a murderer or a cannibal. The story of *Australopithecus* as the first killer, popularized by Ardrey, may be as much a myth as the story of Cain and Abel, but it makes biological sense. A long bone wielded as a club, or a crude stone hand-axe, could be first accidentally and later deliberately lethal in quarrels for dominance amongst the Australopithecines if no inbuilt behaviour patterns had evolved to inhibit the final blow.

Amongst the earliest true men (*Homo erectus*, Peking man) there is evidence that human skulls were opened after death, presumably to eat the brains. Cannibalism would be a natural development in a hunting carnivore without an inborn constraint on intraspecific conflict. Obviously, some pattern of restraint within the family or immediate group would have to develop as a sheer necessity for species survival, but it need not have held for individuals who were strangers to the group. It has often been remarked, by Gorer for example, that many groups of people apply the word for man only to members of their own tribe. Outsiders have another name and, by implication, are less than human and not subject to the taboo on killing that applies within the tribe.

This situation applied widely amongst the Highland peoples of New Guinea, and although the available weapons, which included bows and arrows, spears and polished stone axes, were much more advanced, there were probably some real analogies to early hominid behaviour. Even at the present time there are regions in West Irian where the early pattern of ritualized warfare still holds. Gardner has recently described and illustrated the culture and warlike practices of the Dani, a tribe of mountain people of the Baliem Valley region. The valley is a large one, occupied by some 50,000 people, divided into about a dozen military alliances, each a potential enemy to any other group on its periphery. Every man is a warrior, and the boys learn skill with weapons as the main component of their play. War is an essential part of their culture, the ostensible reason for its continuance being the need to avenge a death, largely because otherwise ghosts would pester the villages. Most battles are formalized affairs; bows and arrows are used and spears thrown from a distance of thirty to fifty yards. Hand-to-hand fighting does not occur and an experienced, alert and agile man can dodge any missile coming in his direction. But sometimes he will be unfortunate. An average battle, involving one to two hundred on each side, will result in one or two men killed in action and eight or ten wounded, of whom some will subsequently die of infection. Like the automobile road-toll in the West, it is a mortality that can readily be tolerated by the community. Throughout the Highlands of New Guinea, this type of perpetual peripheral war, which included small-scale raids and ambushes as well as the formal battles, was the main interest and excitement of the men's lives. Characteristically, each warrior put on his head-dress of bird-of-paradise plumes and made his body glisten with pig-grease as a necessary preliminary to battle.

The hill people of New Guinea are totally illiterate and they had probably been present in the country for 15,000 years before European or any other significant outside contact. Somewhere along the way they developed, or borrowed, the techniques of growing yams and sweet potatoes, of making polished stone axes and using bow and arrow. Their social behaviour, however, could well represent the biological norm of the primitive descendants of *Australopithecus.*

In the well-controlled areas of the Eastern Highlands there have been no tribal wars for nearly twenty years, but the men still find little that seems worth doing, apart from making and decorating their traditional weapons and donning their head-dresses and war-paint for sing-sings and war dances. The first step towards understanding war is to realize that young (and older) men find it easy and enjoyable to use weapons effectively. Anyone who has seen something of the New Guinea Highlands will find it easy to believe that.

To call man the tool-making animal is a euphemism; weapons came before tools, and the most important use of tools has always been to make better weapons.

In the same Pliocene breccias that contain bones of *Australopithecus,* there are also baboon skulls. The two primate species lived at the same environment and their social structure may well have been similar. Baboons are ground-dwellers walking on four feet but with powerful jaws and an intelligence probably not greatly inferior to that of *Australopithecus.* Modern baboons move in companies over a certain range of territory with a considerable degree of discipline within the group. Clashes with other groups do not occur in any normal circumstances, but there is a constant need for vigilance against leopards (and farmers with guns!). According to Washburn and de Vore, the centre of authority in a baboon company is a 'senate' of two or three old males who collectively can deal with any ambitious male who tries to usurp leadership, even if he is younger and more vigorous than any one of them. They take the responsibility of locating the danger and make the decisions when an emergency arises.

The situation is almost precisely analogous in the Dani of the New Guinea Highlands. Battles are planned for and directed by a little group of old warriors of high prestige within the allied villages. Leadership amongst primitive people and the immediate pre-human primates has almost certainly always been of this general character. The leaders are older men experienced in and with a record of success in war.

It is characteristic of elderly men, and particularly of elderly men acting as a group, that they should be conservative. In New Guinea, everything suggests that the general pattern of life has remained unchanged for thousands of years. Peripheral warfare of limited intensity of the type I have described has probably been mainly responsible for the fragmentation of the people into five hundred or more linguistic groups and the total absence of any sense of larger nationality.

In the larger world, things developed differently, war became a more serious matter and weapons and ways of using them evolved more rapidly. Decisive defeat in war by a group of another culture has always been the major cause of social change, as well as a potent way of enlarging the stock of genes available to the blended population of the dominant group and the survivors of the defeated one. The whole pattern of history has been an irregular enlargement of the units involved in war-like activities, primarily by incorporation of defeated groups into the unit of the victor. Such a process could only be on a very small scale as long as subsistence was at the nomad-hunter or village-garden level, but it became inevitably of progressively larger scale as soon as agriculture made it practicable to store food in large amounts and to support a considerable population in cities. This soon came to include professional soldiers and weapon-makers. So, with a thousand variations dependent on racial character, climate and terrain, the skill and ruthlessness of leaders, history began.

Loyalty is a necessary corollary of leadership; patriotism is what makes wars popular. Something more needs to be said about group formation and intra-group relationships, particularly as it bears on the concept of individual and group territories.

There are many different reasons why it should favour the survival of a mammalian species that its members should live in larger or smaller groups. The most important is as a means of protection against predators. A single antelope, especially a young one, is wholly defenceless against lion or leopard. As a member of a herd, the multiplicity of targets may confuse the predator and often allow the whole group to escape from any particular attack. Sometimes the potential prey can, when in close formation, present an invulnerability against, or even a positive threat to the attacker. Most of the large ungulates, buffalo, wild horses, elephants and wild pigs, can ensure the virtual safety of their young in this fashion. On the other side of the predator and prey relationships are the packs of wolves and hunting-dogs. Here the organization into a group makes much simpler the standard manoeuvre of cutting out from the herd a young or decrepit individual and so neutralizing the advantage that the food species gains from *its* group behaviour.

The advantages of group or pack structure are evident, but there is still the question of antagonism between groups to be considered. Group antagonisms are universal, or nearly so, in human societies and with some partial exceptions, such as the extended family groups of chimpanzees, it is also evident in animal groups whose movements are liable to bring them in contact with other groups of the same species. Rats are viciously intolerant of strangers, according to Lorenz, and there are descriptions of antagonism between con-specific groups of baboons, howler monkeys, and other species. The simplest and probably the correct reason for inter-group antagonism derives directly from the hierarchical structure within the group. The stability of the group depends on each individual knowing his social rating in regard to at least the significant upper-level members of the group. To any leader or potential candidate for leadership within the group, each visible male member of an alien group is a possible rival whose quality can only be assessed by actual fighting. This situation can be resolved in one of several ways. Rats will fight fiercely with lethal intent; baboon companies carefully avoid each other, if it is at all possible; howler monkeys take up positions at the edge of their territories and howl at each other. The rules vary according to circumstance. For instance, amongst rhesus monkeys the reaction of troop A may be to give way when it meets troop B, but to force troop C to withdraw. The leaders apparently learn the relative status of their troops, just as each monkey knows its own status within the group.

It seems likely that the group behaviour of *Australopithecus* initially resembled that of baboons. Leopards may have been their major threat, and one can imagine that a group of little proto-men using stones and other primitive weapons could usually send a leopard to seek quarry with more easily predictable behaviour. As a hunter in his turn, *Australopithecus* would find even greater virtues in group organization, particularly with the progressive development of communication by speech.

The use of language is the most uniquely human characteristic. Even the most primitive and isolated groups have relatively elaborate languages and not even the chimpanzee or the gorilla shows anything remotely comparable. There is no conceivable way of establishing how or when language arose, but it is a reasonable guess that as soon as men or ape-men were producing weapons or other artifacts they were also capable of rudimentary speech. As a hunter who anatomically was unfit for hunting, early man must have depended greatly on concerted action and on special stratagems, such as driving animals into natural cul-de-sacs. Capacity for clear communication between individuals at moderate distances would obviously have been of special value in hunting and of even greater importance once inter-group warfare became a significant feature of life.

Social hierarchies can develop in the absence of language, but for any sort of communal activities requiring the use of language for their co-ordination, an accepted heirarchy of dominance becomes essential. At some point, one man must make a decision and the rest must obey automatically. It is a natural extension from the parent-offspring relationship in any mammalian species. Equally, man is descended from earlier primates who, for probably thirty million years, had lived in bands with some or all of the characteristics of the herd common to gregarious animals. The universal characters of group behaviour must have become even more evident in human groups once the members could be held together and interact with each other through speech. The importance of intra-group structure is evident by the wide range of inter-relationships between individuals which in every language can always be specified in words, and the almost invariable existence of special forms of speech appropriate for use in relationships involving superiority and inferiority. Leadership from the top, loyalty and obedience from those lower in the social pyramid, this is what evolutionary experience seems to prescribe as the pattern for group survival. Whether it holds for man as well has only recently come into question. In the Western world it seems that vocal representatives of every under-privileged group demand a destruction of any type of hierarchical structure which seems to their special disadvantage. Social structures that have a manifest usefulness are, however, not easily destroyed. There is a basically similar hierarchical character in organizations that range from the Roman Catholic Church to an ultra-modern research facility like CERN at Geneva, or from General Motors to the service-station on the street corner. All history says that the line of command must run clearly for any but the simplest of group activities.

Social heirarchies are inevitable in any conceivable future and each will tend to be self-perpetuating and obstructive toward any move for intelligent change. There is only one useful rule to be drawn from the behaviour of both animal and human groups. This is that innovation of any sort is only likely to be effective if it is initiated by the leaders. Ideas can come from anyone, but if they are to be effective in a community that is functioning more or less normally, they must be taken up by the educated, the élite, the holders of power. Violence of the masses is an effective agent for change only when society has been disorganized.

There are many different ways of tracing the possible lines by which civilization developed, and it will impress most liberally minded people as showing a lack of balance to concentrate almost wholly on the evolution of weapons and war as the central theme of human evolution and history. This, however, is an approach which has been widely discussed in both scientific and non-scientific circles since it was initiated a long time ago by Arthur Keith and Raymond Dart and popularized more recently in Ardrey's two books, *African Genesis* and *Territorial Imperative*. Lorenz's writings have less explicitly supported the same general thesis. As might be expected, there has been a strong 'back-lash' by anthropologists and psychologists of more idealistic bent. Their main objection, however, seems to have been to the postulation of a 'killer' instinct in man. I have already discussed the equivocal nature of the words 'instinct' and 'instinctive' in their human connotations. Highly elaborate behaviour-patterns in some mammals and birds clearly depend wholly on genetically determined circuits in the nervous system. Most human behaviour can be exemplified in the way a child learns to speak. Around the age of two the child is imitating any sounds made by its parents or siblings and very rapidly begins to use them to convey information. Within another year he is speaking in the language (or languages) of his immediate associates. The child has no inheritance of English or Chinese, but he differs from every other immature animal in possessing by inheritance what is needed to allow him to develop rapidly, from listening to what others say, the capacity to use language as they do. One additional point needs to be added: some children learn their own language much more rapidly than others. There are people who learn additional languages with ease, others find it virtually impossible. The question of whether there is an instinct for homicide in man is basically meaningless. What is meaningful, however, is the statement that, through hominid evolution and throughout the cultural evolution of man, there has been survival value to human groups if young males found it easy and gratifying to learn how to use weapons for killing. No more specific explanation is required.

To a biologist, the only possible attitude to history is that it should describe the changing distribution of people according to number and genetic constitution over the globe. Once the lowered sea-levels of the last glaciation allowed human entry into the Americas and Australia, any major change before the European entry into the empty lands of the nineteenth century was by war or its concomitants, such as the slave-trade. Political history has always been military history. Infectious disease, seasonal shortage of food and recurrent famine were very important checks on population growth once urbanization developed. They probably caused many more untimely deaths than were directly due to war, but famine and pestilence were the traditional and necessary concomitants of war.

Success in war has depended primarily on the invention of more effectively lethal weapons and new techniques of battle. Bronze made better weapons than chipped stone or hardened wood. Iron was better than bronze, and steel a refinement on cast-iron. Most of the major inventions found usage in war and were probably produced primarily to increase the military competence of the group involved. From the wheel and the primitive methods of metallurgy to the development of explosives, of effective aircraft and of the atom bomb and space vehicles it was the promise of military effectiveness that gave an inventor the facilities to elaborate his dream.

Zoologists have spoken of the enormous growth of the human brain in the last two million years as one of the major mysteries of evolution. The cerebral cortex, the new brain of the higher mammals, the great computer, doubled in size in those 100,000 generations. That enlargement brought with it the skills of the artisan and the soldier and the potentialities of art, philosophy and science, even of goodness, of altruism without dominance. If one believes in evolution, there must have been some intense advantage in selective survival to any group of early hominids whose brain sizes and intelligence were increasing faster than in other populations of their species. I can see only one likely way in which that selection pressure could be exerted, by the use of intelligence to devise new ways to kill those of the species who were less intelligent. The alternative could be that for a prolonged period, perhaps between the time of *Australopithecus* and Cro-

Magnon man, some 20,000 years ago, the survival of the developing species depended time and again on the ability of one family, or a very small group, to survive, by the use of unusual intelligence, catastrophes that eliminated the rest of their community.

Always present as a background to this discussion is the recognition of the extraordinary, the psycho-pathological quality of human history. Winwood Reade wrote of the martyrdom of man and, amongst contemporary writers, Arthur Koestler has written, in large part from his own experience, much about the insanity of men with power. Like many others, he feels that there is something outside the order of Nature in human evil. In an essay on the Predicament of Man (1968) he opened by saying: 'that the native equipment of *Homo sapiens* may contain some built-in error or deficiency which would predispose him to self-destruction. More precisely, that evolution has equipped our species with a type of brain in which affect-based beliefs are dissociated from and in perpetual conflict with the reasoning intellect. The result, as we see it, is a split-minded or schizophrenic mentality which seems to be inherent in man's condition and is reflected in his absurd and tortured history.'

When he comes to the point of asking what, specifically, has gone wrong in the course of human evolution, he discards the notion that aggressiveness, as such, is the basic fault. Rather, in his view, man has 'too strong a biological need to belong, to attach himself to a person, a group or idea, to transcend the claustrophobic confines of his self.' Koestler wonders whether this sprang from 'the increased dependence on solidarity and co-operation of our primate ancestors when they turned into carnivorous hunters of prey bigger and faster than themselves.'

This clearly is related to my own approach, but still seems rather superficial in the sense that it fails to account for the exceptional development of the 'new brain', the neopallium, during a million years or so. Perhaps an even greater difficulty, which I believe Koestler also recognizes, is the extreme range of variation in the size of the human brain and in the character and effectiveness of its function. The brain size, in round figures, changed something like this:

			cc
Australopithecus	1,500,000 years ago		500
Homo erectus	700,000–400,000 years ago		1,000
Homo sapiens	Present	(1,100–1,800)	1,400

There is only a small correlation between intelligence and cranial capacity amongst modern Europeans, but this cannot invalidate the broad evolutionary concept that, during the million years between *Australopithecus* and the earliest men, intelligence and brain size increased *pari passu*. There are no recognizable stone artifacts found with *Australopithecus*, and most authorities would postulate that weapon- and tool-making and the development of speech were functionally associated with the enlargement of the brain.

When Australopithicines, probably of two distinct species, lived in South Africa, baboons of a type similar to those of the present day were common in the same areas. Both genera were presumably adequately fitted to survive in the late Pliocene or early Pleistocene environment. Since then, however, the baboon brain has changed little, but the hominids developed into modern man. There is a first-rate problem for the geneticists here, which may be worth a little speculative attention that springs from one of my own technical interests.

Those of us who are concerned with immunology are deeply committed to seek an understanding of the genetics of antibody specificity. In one way or another, a man—or a rabbit—can produce, by what must be basically a genetic process, many thousands of different sorts of antibody. Quite clearly, multiple genes transmitted from both parents are involved, plus some additional genetic process at work in the differentiating cell lines that lead to the cells concerned with antibody production, and the like. This has no special significance for the sort of human problems we are interested in, but more than one biologist has wondered whether, when we understand the genetics of antibody formation—and this may be no more than five years away—it may not provide important leads for an attack on the much more difficult problems of the evolution and the embryonic development of brain function in man. There is little doubt that in the brain, on top of an elaborate set of basic genetic programming for structure and function, there has been a high level of mutational activity in the genes concerned to cover the enormous genetically based range of general and special abilities. But it is equally evident that the detailed structure of the brain as 'computer' is not laid down rigorously by the genetic information in the fertilized egg. In a real sense, it builds itself by its own functioning during embryonic development and early life. Evolution seems to have found it necessary to confer a potentially dangerous lability on the genetic processes which build up the giant nerve knot of the brain and provide the basis for its eventual function.

Koestler may be right in laying special stress on the human capacity for loyalty, yet one wonders whether what passes for loyalty is not most often merely an intelligent response to self-interest. If the alternative to loyal support for the Viet Cong is a bullet through the back of the head, a villager chooses survival. One senses that with a change in the general approach to authority in affluent countries since 1945, automatic loyal support for national war can no longer be counted on. Maybe it never could. Through most of Europe's history before the Napoleonic wars, patriotic nationalism was inconspicuous. A large proportion of the armies were composed of mercenaries and it is unlikely that their sense of loyalty to their leaders was any more than that of a bandit troop or pirate crew, sufficient to convert a randomly gathered group of men into an effective means of exerting compulsion through violence, but no more.

The heterogeneity of human beings at every level is one of the unique characteristics of our species. Most of that diversity can be traced to differences in brain and behaviour. For the present, colour can be left aside; within each of the major racial groups, Australoids, Mongoloids, Negroids and Caucusoids and their mixed derivatives, there are almost equivalent divergencies. Biological differences regularly tend to be associated with isolation. It is the nature of things that, in times before civilization, human beings should be distributed in smaller or larger groups occupying relatively isolated areas, an island, a fertile valley, an estuary, and having only rare encounters with people outside the group.

With the lability of the human nervous system it is inevitable that, when a population divides for any reason into two populations which remain isolated from one another, a process of independent change will begin. Especially if a 'colony' develops from a small founding group and finds it possible to enlarge rapidly, the new population will possess a significantly different distribution of genes from the parent population. Genetics and cultural tradition are both conservative agents, but mutation and innovation constantly occur. In a few score generations, the languages spoken may retain similar structure, but they may be almost mutually incomprehensible and there will be slight or great differences in almost every aspect of how things are done. Each community will regard the others as strangers and the everlasting process of personalizing an out-group as a competitor or an enemy will be in action again.

The lability of language must have been a potent agent in facilitating the process of fragmenting man into a multitude of antagonistic tribal groupings. History in every country begins with the reversal of that process by military conquest. Conquest had important biological features. In the defeated group, men were either killed, enslaved, or in one day or another made part of the military forces of the conqueror, the women became additional concubines for the invaders and in the next generation two gene pools had come together to give new genetic potentialities. In a similar fashion, the conquerors' language, often greatly modified by borrowings from the defeated, became a common tongue. The basic process, with an infinite range of variations in detail, has gone on throughout history. Apart from what is probably only a temporary aberration of the acceptance of dozens of small independent nation-states in the last twenty years, the process has been one of progressive enlargement. So far, the nation-state is, in Gorer's words, the limit to the size of the pack within which killing is murder.

In 1967, Robert Ardrey published a highly readable book called

The Territorial Imperative which introduced the general reader
to the concept of territory in relation to animal behaviour. The
occupation and defence of territory by birds and animals takes
various forms and is nearly always closely associated with reproductive behaviour. Almost every well-studied example provides
a very interesting story and Ardrey tells many of them superbly.
It is only when he applies the ethological concept of territory so
whole-heartedly to human affairs that most academic sociologists
and psychologists part company from him. In their view, it is
quite an illegitimate extension of the concept to ascribe the
sudden outburst of nationalistic patriotic fervour that swept
America after Pearl Harbor to the instinctive response that 'our'
territory was being invaded. I should agree that this was an over-
simplification, but I would still go along with Ardrey in seeing
human relevance in the relative uniformity of territorial behaviour
over a very wide range of vertebrates from fish to antelopes and
howler monkeys.

The general concept derives from the British ornithologist,
Howard's work on the behaviour of song-birds in the breeding
season. Using the chaffinch as an example, the story is, in essentials, as follows: In early Spring, a male bird stakes out a territory
of the order of an acre, with at least a tree or two to serve as look-
outs and song-posts. The chaffinch's song is an intimation of his
presence to a female and a challenge to males to keep off his
territory. The presence of a male in effective control of a territory
is the only attraction that persuades a female to accept and set
up nest-building with him. Once the territory is established, the
chaffinch will attack any other male chaffinch which crosses its
invisible boundary, but has no interest in other species. Any
conflict within the territory is invariably won by the defender,
but if he, after victory, transgresses on the other's territory, the
tables are immediately turned. Only in the narrow indeterminate
no-man's-land are the contenders evenly matched.

There are much more elaborate territorial rituals in other types
of bird, particularly in polygamous forms like sage-grouse or
ruff, or in the more exotic bower-birds and birds-of-paradise in
New Guinea and Australia. Mammalian territorial behaviour can

be almost equally complex, but, for our purpose, only the non-human primates need any consideration. Perhaps the most interesting aspect of all is that amongst primate species there is almost every possible type of social structure to be seen. All show some degree of ranking within the group, but the degree of dominance of one individual over another varies greatly from species to species. A gorilla troop may include several adult males, but they are peaceable animals and the leader, always an old silver-backed male, has a virtual sinecure. They wander extensively and claim no territory. Chimpanzee groups have a defined feeding-area but do not defend it. Baboons form closely disciplined groups in which control is exercised by a small mutually tolerant group of old males. In most areas of Africa, a baboon troop has a well-defined territory over which it ranges. Intrusion into another group's territory is so rare that one must assume that the territory is not defended but maintained by a mutual instinctively based taboo on intrusion into an alien territory. The last primate to be mentioned is the Central American howler monkey whose bands live in internal amity but defend their territory vigorously by howling at any adjacent group across the border. No other violence seems to be necessary.

Much more can be read in Ardrey, but perhaps the only vital aspects of territory in animals that have a bearing on human affairs are: first, that a territory is defended only against members of the same species; second, that territorial behaviour always has some evolutionary advantage in relation to the particular ecological niche of the species that adopts it, and is correspondingly variable in form; and third, that, with the rarest of exceptions, when combat occurs within a territory the occupier-defender always wins.

Primitive human groups, likewise, adjust their attitude to territory according to their ecological situation. In arid country which can provide only a difficult living for a small population, as for the Australian Aborigines or the Bushmen of the Kalahari desert, contact between groups is rare and mostly amicable. With almost equally primitive peoples in the New Guinea Highlands the position is quite different. The fertile high valleys are relatively densely populated and the land in the neighbourhood of a village is regarded as being owned by the group and will be defended by them. At various places on the periphery, however, there were no-man's-lands where semi-ritualized battles with neighbouring groups took place. Within the tribal area, families have special rights of ownership of their own food-producing garden.

Rights to land are cherished and quarrelled over. Once pacification and control by the Administration has been established, most of the patrol-officer's work is in attempting to record and regularize rights to land. European settlement can, in general, only involve land for which there is no substantial native claim or which is bought for a fair price and with the voluntary consent of the accepted owners. The discovery and exploitation of minerals in the Territory has provoked complex social difficulties. Tribal and individual owners are as interested in driving a hard bargain as any European and, perhaps, a little prone to confer traditional and religious sanctions on what is mainly plain cupidity.

I was talking, not long ago, with a Bougainville man about the troubles they were having in this matter. He was a medical-assistant whose English was fairly competent. The attitude of his people, so he said, could be summed in one of his people's proverbs, which was approximately:

A man is not a fish, he does not swim in the sea;
A man is not a bird, he does not fly in the air;
But a man has land for his garden which will
pass on to his family forever.

One wonders to what extent that attitude remains amongst those who live in advanced countries. The proportion of the population actually engaged in agriculture has been steadily falling. In the more desirable parts of Australia most farms stay in the family and pass to a son or son-in-law, but the rest of the family move to the cities. Most economists consider that the land, when it comes on the market, is over-valued. The capital required to buy a farm could be used to produce a considerably higher income than can be won from the farm, which suggests that, for some people, there is still an additional emotional satisfaction to be had from owning and working one's own land. Among Australian city-dwellers there is still an overwhelming preference for the single family home with a garden, but the owner's attitude to that little piece of territory is much the same as that of the dog which he usually keeps. 'This is mine—in its own way it is an index of my position in society—I am rather proud of it, and if I don't want you to come in, you stay out.' But with a ten per cent rise in salary, he will move happily to another suburb or another city.

Patriotism probably has a component based on primitive attachment to the land, but the image that the average man carries of his own nation-state has many other components. It is personalized as having ownership and power over many desirable things, of which the land and its products form a highly visible but relatively small component, but which also include 'our' factories, 'our' mines, 'our' tennis-players, and even 'our' scientists or artists. As the Continental Shelf became accessible to the oil-driller, as well as the fisherman, national rights were claimed for as far out from the coastline as the country had the naval power to enforce. Activities here can also be included in the image of the country and therefore to be defended. Once, however, there was support for Woodrow Wilson's doctrine of freedom of the seas. In any country there will only be a very small minority with a vested interest in contesting internationalization of the seas beyond a reasonable five- or ten-mile limit. In any approach toward one world, this may be the softest area at which to press in the first stages.

I am a professional scientist—retired from the bench and more interested now in ideas than experiments. Science, just as much now as in 1947, is central to all my thinking, but I fancy that the accent has changed in those more than twenty years. In those days, I defined the scientific method as 'the effective use of human thought and behaviour so that some desired end may be successfully obtained. This behaviour, and the mental processes associated with it, must be capable of being formulated in words or other symbols sufficiently precise to allow another individual of equivalent intelligence and dexterity to effectively reproduce the thought and behaviour.'

Even then, and much more so today, that definition, though still basically valid, requires extension and qualification. The desired end nowadays is more subtle than a new source of energy or a new mouse-trap. In today's laboratory, what is desired is usually the answer that will fill a gap in the accepted structure of knowledge. It is immaterial whether filling the gap will either directly or indirectly provide health, comfort or wealth to other members of the community.

The real requirements are probably to be expressed in some such terms as:

1 The existence of the gap in knowledge must be evident, either from a logical consideration of published work in the field or, more frequently, because of the recognition by the scientist himself of some experimental result or observation which is not covered by currently accepted generalizations.

2   The scientist must provide a hypothesis, or a series of alternative hypotheses, which can be tested by methods which are either immediately available or can be devised. Science, in Medawar's phrase, is the art of the soluble. A theory or a hypothesis which does not suggest ways by which it can be proved to be wrong or which fails to suggest new lines of experimental work is worthless.

3   Proof of a hypothesis will always be provisional, but the factual data obtained in testing it should stand. The combination of verifiable observations and their logical interpretation must be accepted as significant by the body of scientists interested in the relevant field. Such acceptance will raise the professional status of the scientist responsible for the work.

The time may already be here when much scientific achievement has exactly the same status as achievement in art or in creative literature. It is the fruit of an opportunity given to the gifted—by a society that can fulfil its material needs with ease —to gain satisfaction, recognition and reward by doing something supremely well.

This, however, is a modern and sophisticated approach which is not even fully acceptable to scientists themselves. Many would prefer the public image that the justification for scientific work is to produce what people need or desire. Historically, there can be no doubt whatever that this was what led, through craftsmanship, to science and art.

With my first utilitarian definition of the scientific method in mind, we can start by looking at the work of an early maker of weapons. The traditional method of producing a flint arrow-head in Neolithic times was a relatively precise series of manoeuvres capable of being taught to others and producing a very uniform type of manufactured object. The knowledge and craftsmanship involved in making an arrow-head, weaving a basket or striking fire from flint is essentially scientific and it is from activities of this sort that modern scientific activity is directly derived. The derivation of science from craftsmanship can be readily seen by looking at the commonest of situations in industrial practice. A certain process provides some object of human desire; one day, for no obvious reason, the process breaks down, the product, for one reason or another, is worthless. There is immediately a need to find out what has gone wrong. Even a primitive craftsman will tend to look for every possible change in circumstances; to go over the differences one by one and to try in a crude way to test each of them separately. Sooner or later, he will find where the weakness lay and, if he is a little more intelligent than the next man, he may see how he can consistently avoid such a mishap in future and, by passing on the information to other craftsmen, change the traditional process of manufacture a little. Such things also happen in modern factories, and here the scientific attack on this standard type of problem merely involves a more detailed analysis of the difference between the two situations and refines the methods for testing experimentally which of the factors possibly concerned are significant.

The experimental scientist is in a direct line of descent from the mediaeval, or even from the Neolithic craftsman. Artisan or scientist, he has had to deal, not with the vagaries of human interactions, but with tractable things—metal, wood and fibres, living plants and animals. Improvements in man's handling of these things have gone on continuously since the beginnings of civilization. Civilization, in fact, only became possible when the development of agriculture, with the possibility of storing food as grain for relatively long periods, allowed substantial numbers of people to be provided with the necessities of life by the work of others. This allowed the development of an increasing number of special categories of people with no direct part in the production of food. They included secular or religious ruling groups and at least a nucleus of full-time soldiers and servants. More important from the present point of view were the specialist craftsmen. Initially, the metal-workers, the armourers, were presumably the most important, but with the development of a ruling-class there was automatically a living available for any craftsman with special talents. Skill in manipulation varies greatly from person to person and it is always easy to recognize that one weapon, one beaker, or one piece of woven cloth is better, more desirable than another. With the concentration of power and the need for display of the trappings of power it became more and more important for the palace or other seat of power to patronize many craftsmen of every type. One has only to look at the products of classic Egyptian and Cretan civilizations to recognize how rapidly the craftsmen of antiquity invented and perfected the basic forms of household utensils and furniture, of weapons and tools that were to last almost unchanged for millenia. It is equally true that other craftsmen of the same era devised the basic forms of representational and decorative art. Skill and knowledge within the crafts were passed on by apprenticeship, with each generation modifying and often improving on its predecessor's work. It is probable that, through the whole of history, there has been an unbroken sequence of traditional skills in every field of craftsmanship. The craftsmen's castes or guilds were quite distinct from the ruling-classes and from the literate priesthood.

At every stage, some men have been concerned to use everything they have learnt from others and their own innovations to produce something better, something which will delight them, bring them prestige and be sold at a profit. Another group of men have been interested in the how and why of things, the reasons for the regularities of Nature, the administrative problems of allotting land or goods to individuals, which gave rise to geometry and arithmetic and the progressive elaboration or refinement of religious tradition to cover new areas of discovery or interest. In the Classic Age of Greece, the foundations were laid of all the modes of thought, including mathematics, that would be applied to the development of science, but the philosophers did not discover the experimental method.

What can be called the scientific period began in the late Middle Ages, when men of the literate upper-classes began to develop an interest in natural phenomena and craft techniques, as well as in history and politics, or in theology, philosophy and mathematics. Men with leisure to think and write about such matters would naturally be ready to apply the same style of thought to problems and processes less directly concerning them as soon as such matters became either fashionable or important.

An educated class of merchants, ship-owners and financiers must necessarily have been concerned, to some extent at least, with the various crafts which produced and moved their merchandise, just as politically powerful individuals were concerned with the quality of the weapons in the hands of their soldiers.

In some such way we find the modern scientific approach gradually arising, in large part as a result of the growing appreciation by the ruling-classes of the importance of craftsmanship for war and commerce. There had, however, been a tradition of scholarship somewhere in the world ever since the days of Greece and over the centuries a substantial body of natural philosophy had been developed to cover mathematics, astronomy and the simple observational sciences. This scholarly learning was waiting to be applied to the examination of craft processes and the many new natural phenomena provided by the voyages to America and elsewhere. The craftsman's side and the philosopher's side began to fuse when apothecaries, clock-makers and glass-workers were called on to provide materials and apparatus with which the gentlemen-philosophers could 'make experiments'. It was at this stage that the Royal Society and the other scientific academies of Europe came into existence.

It may be worth recalling that, in 1662, two years after the Royal Society was founded, Robert Hooke was appointed without salary 'to furnish the Society, every day they met, with three or four considerable experiments'. Hooke maintained close contact with the best of London's craftsmen, instrument-makers, clock- and watch-makers, metal- and wood-workers, and himself became a skilled mechanic. Always, since the days of Boyle and Hooke, the natural philosopher has worked with technicians or been his own instrument-maker. Progress was rapid as instrumentation was progressively improved and mathematics became more sophisticated. Discovery was a self-accelerating process, but although natural philosophy made use of the best work of the artisans from the seventeenth century onward, there was little contribution of academic science to industry before the later decades of the nineteenth century. Then, first Germany and eventually and dominantly the United States, turned the full power of science on to industrial innovation and production. In 1969, we have put men on the moon and brought them safely back to earth. Material progress, through science and technology, has swung, like so much else, into an exponential course that will clearly end in chaos. But that can be left for a later section.

As we move into the 1970s there is a deeper questioning of the human values of science than at any time in history. Progress is no longer a universally popular word.

The number of scientists and the volume of published scientific work increased at an exponential rate from the days when the Royal Society was founded till three centuries later. Through all that period it could be said: 'There are many more scientists working now than in all the generations of scientists before us taken together.' The figure now has grown to millions, it is still growing, but from 1967–68 the exponential growth of science in the United States had to stop. From now onwards, expenditure on science will keep in step with growth of the economy as a whole.

At no stage has there ever been a lack of problems for study. Today there is no one amongst my friends still actively working at the laboratory bench who is not eager to attract more bright young Ph.D students to help him tidy up the scientific field in which he is working. The optimists proclaim that there can be no conceivable end to the acquisition of knowledge by the scientific method, and that in each addition to knowledge there is a potentiality of direct human benefit. Others of us are not so sure. Discovery cannot go on for ever and I believe that we may already be over-supplied with laboratory scientists. There is always something for them to do, but many are involved in minutiae, tidying up loose ends, picking up a few grains of knowledge from some well-garnered field. It is illuminating to watch how, as soon as a new phenomenon is recognized in any field of science, there is a swift mobilization of dozens or hundreds of scientists who can cheerfully leave their current research activity to join in the gold-rush. Two recent examples come to mind: There was first, Bartlett's completely unexpected discovery in 1962 that xenon, one of the inert gases which every chemist knew would combine with nothing, produced a well-defined compound with fluorine. Within two years the field had been thoroughly explored and a full theoretical doctrine of the chemical reactivity of the noble gases established. A second example comes from my own area of interest. A certain obscure disease of the brain affecting children had been known for many years, with no clue as to its cause. Then, following a hint from French electron-microscopists, virologists in Belfast found antibody to measles virus in the cerebrospinal fluid of three such cases early in 1967. The implication was that the disease represented some type of chronic measles virus infection of the brain. This was a wholly new idea with exciting possible significance for the pathology of virus disease. Less than nine months later, the first full-scale conference on the disease, attended by nearly one hundred scientists, was held and the proceedings published in March 1968. Clearly, there are more competent scientists than there are exciting—and prestige-conferring —problems for study.

In one sense, I believe that it is undoubtedly true that, in a thousand years' time, historians will speak of an age of scientific discovery starting with Galileo at 1586 and finishing, perhaps, no more than four centuries later. I believe that 99 per cent of the scientific generalizations that bear on human affairs have already been made. This does not in any way diminish the importance of science, but it will call for a very different approach.

In the field of physical science, it is already possible to achieve anything that can be shown to be physically possible in principle, provided that an adequate concentration of effort and intelligence can be brought to bear. The safe return of men with rock samples from the moon is the supreme verification of that statement.

No such statement can be made about biological or social objectives. I have said elsewhere that I can see no likelihood that the application of science to medicine will ever provide a means of curing cancer, of preventing or curing serious autoimmune disease, or a way of eliminating genetic disease. Living processes at the genetic and cellular levels bring in a wholly different order of complexity from what exists in the inorganic physical world.

Intellectual, emotional and social processes in man present even a greater degree of complexity and difficulty. At this level, each problem is essentially unique. Experience of the past is helpful, but it can hardly ever allow a genuinely scientific approach to the social and psychological difficulties of mental deficiency, psychoses and psychosomatic disease, delinquency, crime and war.

The application of research and of established scientific knowledge to human benefit presents very different aspects, according to what is regarded as of human benefit. Virtually all the great scientific developments of the last fifty years that impinge on the life of the ordinary man are non-biological and have either been invented specifically for war or have been brought to a practical level for use in war: jet aircraft, rocket propulsion, satellite communication, computers, nuclear fission, nuclear fusion. In a peaceful world we should need none of them—though jet aircraft as a means of travel and computers to allow social organization could not now be abolished. As long as war persists, progress in producing ever more lethally efficient weapons and systems will go on without regard for exhaustion of resources or fouling of the environment.

In the affluent world, the objective of industrial activity is to produce and sell things and materials that people desire or can be stimulated to desire. The standard industrial attitude to science is that its application should either:

(a) allow something new and desirable to be produced at a profit: television, transistor radios, tape-recorders, ball-point pens, contraceptive pills; or
(b) raise the competitive status of a product either by improving its quality or lowering its cost of manufacture.

There can be no question that the application of science to the more efficient production of what people want has been broadly beneficial to the community. Standard of living has risen proportionately to the intensity of industrial competition and the use made of science and technology. Competitive capitalism has easily outpaced the socialist regimes.

Yet with the success of Apollo XI in mind, one wonders whether any more science is needed to provide what people want. Intelligent manipulation of known principles and materials and control by computer techniques put men on the moon and could accomplish any other objective that is physically permissible. What is needed is not new principles but the application of what is known to the urgent tasks for the world as a whole. There are far too many research scientists and too few good inventors and technicians, if this is a reasonable interpretation of the world's need.

For the present I am not, however, concerned with ethics but with actualities. There is a very large output of academic research in all the universities of the world and there are massive institutes of pure and applied research in every advanced country. As a professional scientist with a strongly academic bias, I must find some satisfying justification for that research.

In 1947, I was naturally much more impressed with the human applications of science than I am after twenty more years of intensive research by an enormously enlarged body of better-trained and better-equipped scientists. I said then:

'There is still an infinite array of human desires and an infinite variety of obstacles to their fulfilment. Each year something of the order of a million scientific papers are published, each giving an account of some investigation of a specific problem. Probably 100,000 of these papers do make a definite new contribution to knowledge. Any one of the facts recorded in the last thirty or forty years output of such papers may be needed for the solution of some practical problem, that is, to satisfy some human desire. The problem at once arises as to how that fact can be found when it is wanted. The answer is, because of the virtues of the scientific generalization. A "law of nature" is a means by which a vast array of facts can be brought together in a fashion which allows their essence to be contained in an ordinary human mind and which provides a guide to the relevant detailed knowledge bearing on a humanly important problem. The function of the scientific generalization is to render knowledge *accessible*.'

All that is, in a sense, still true, but one has only to look through a few numbers of *Nature* or *Science* to realize that the knowledge being made accessible by generalization in 95 per cent or more of the published papers is of interest only to specialist scientists working in the same field. At the present time, I am fascinated by the progress being made in the elucidation of the chemical structure of antibodies and its bearing on the nature of the specificity of immune reactions. An immense amount of money is being spent on such work and there are exciting generalizations becoming apparent. I doubt, however, whether any one of the leading scientists in this field can see the slightest possibility of a 'practical' application of the knowledge when we have it.

Some quite other justification is needed for activity on the chemistry of antibodies, the nature of quasars and the mechanics of continental drift. Those are three of the most exciting areas of science in 1969; none are of the least practical importance. Their real justification lies in the deeper meaning of that vogue word, 'exciting'. For centuries, rulers and whole communities have been ready to provide opportunity for an artist to paint a masterpiece, or for a composer to produce a song-cycle, and to pay them well for the aesthetic experience, the excitement, that they give to the people capable of recognizing their excellence. The scientist capable of what his peers can recognize as a first-rate contribution is in exactly the same situation. The chance, however small, that in addition his work may have some practical application is immaterial—a bonus to be received gratefully, if it eventuates, but wholly secondary.

But there is another aspect of scientific work which can be made just as forcibly as I did in 1947. Science is an activity carried out by human beings, on the whole by men of higher-than-average intelligence, but by men with all the normal complement of the basic behaviour-patterns. As in all activities, the urges associated with dominance-order are important and constitute perhaps the most essential part of the whole mental attitude of the scientist.

Science has been successful because, more than in any other field, socially valuable activity, that is, successful discovery or elucidation, is automatically associated with a rise in the dominance-order concerned. Unsound work is always subject to criticism and experimental refutation, and the more important the discovery claimed, the more rapidly it will be refuted if it is wrong. Success in science has high public prestige and every organized centre of scientific research is eager to provide opportunity to a worker of proved capacity. So it happens that success automatically provides opportunity for better work still. Promotion is promotion by merit, merit being defined quite simply in terms of the value placed on a man's work by contemporary scientists of repute who are interested in and capable of criticizing the field. When a man gains in scientific prestige, when he rises in his chosen hierarchy of dominance, that rise is likely to induce less antagonism by those overpassed than in most other such orders. It must not be forgotten, too, that in science there is an infinite number of dominance-orders: whenever a scientist produces a sound new paper he is able to feel that in his own particular corner of science (however small it may be) he is at that moment at the very top of the corresponding dominance-order. He has a more accurate knowledge of that corner of science than anybody else in the world. This is much more conducive to contentment than any place in a rigid hierarchy. Distinction in science (or for that matter in the creative arts) is, or can be attained without major resentment by others. It may be that the essence of successful organization within any functioning human group is to maintain a dominance-order by methods which do not provoke resentment.

With this angle of human satisfaction by success and the recognition of success by their peers in mind, we can look again at the position of scientists after the 'Age of Scientific Discovery' is over. The picture of academic science of the future is already beginning to clarify.

One of the great social necessities of an affluent society is to ensure that as large a proportion of the highly intelligent people who are born into the community find occupation that makes use of their intelligence and *feels* worth doing. One interesting diagnosis of the student revolt of the 1960s, which significantly does not normally involve students of science or the science-based professions, is due to Bettelheim. He sees the active leaders as highly intelligent individuals from well-to-do homes with permissive liberal-minded parents. They see the weaknesses of the society they are embedded in, and having no thought of the possibility of physical poverty and a conscious or unconscious contempt for their too-permissive fathers, they undertake the sort of university courses in politics and sociology which promise understanding and solution of social difficulties. In Bettelheim's view, the recognition by the intelligent of the basic futility of current academic work and teaching in the social sciences is the main factor predisposing to revolt. To be a leader in revolt probably needs, in addition, that paranoid tendency which is not uncommon amongst the highly intelligent. By contrast, a man doing science has no doubt about the reality of the processes and theories which he studies and, whether his post-graduate career is in academic research or industry, he has tangible things to think about and relatively high expectations of technical achievement and recognition. Such men do not become rebels.

Whenever I have said that science is no longer necessary in an affluent society, it has been only in terms of its being the fairy-godmother bringing 'goodies' for the ordinary man. The function of the research organization as a means of providing a very satisfying way of life for men of high intelligence and capacity is an entirely different matter. We all pay lip-service to the desirability of disarmament and the elimination of war, but any sudden cut-down on the production of weapons and all that it entails would be disastrous to the millions thrown out of employment. Those would include large numbers of scientists and the best technologists in the world. One of the main concomitants of disarmament would have to be the provision of a steadily increasing number of centres of scientific and other high-grade intellectual activities.

I do not foresee any serious diminution in the capacity of scientific work to capture and hold a man's complete interest, even after all the eternal generalizations are made. There will always be endless fascination in phenomena in progress, in things that are happening in 'real time'. This year it was announced that Australia was purchasing a $10 million complex of computers to allow the meteorological service to make full use of satellite photographs and other new types of information in their forecasts. The weather involves mainly the thermo-dynamics and hydro-dynamics of air- and water-vapour as influenced by solar energy and the configurations of the earth's surface. There are probably only a few secondary 'laws' to be discovered, but the day-to-day elucidation of the process can provide high-level occupation for a steadily increasing number of scientists for any foreseeable future.

Again, to use an Australian example, there is the urgent need for the establishing of a continuing biological survey of Australia. During my presidency of the Australian Academy we pressed, so far with no more than expressions of sympathy in response, for the establishment of such a survey by the Commonwealth Government. It would involve gaining a systematic knowledge of the distribution of mammals, birds, insects and other animals over the continent, and similar botanical studies—*and keeping the knowledge up to date*. Opening up of new land, droughts and other climatic changes, new patterns of land use—all of these things will change fauna and flora. Ecologists and a wide range of specialist scientists can be kept happy indefinitely. Similar conditions apply in regard to the epidemiology of disease, particularly the impact of social developments on psychosomatic disease. In industry, there will always be day-to-day changes required and one can foresee major ones arising as basic materials have to be obtained from less-convenient sources.

In one way or another, we shall be able to keep our scientists employed in at least their present numbers and with almost equally satisfying work.

In this book I have deliberately left out of consideration most of the pleasanter aspects of human life—love and affection, generosity and sympathy, courage and self-denial, the appreciation of beauty. This is simply because in any tolerable structure of society these qualities would persist. They present no conceivable threat to the good life. To be consistent, the fine arts would also not merit discussion. Yet one often has a sense that, along with the things that I am primarily concerned with, modern pictorial art is also on an exponential course that will end (or is ending) in chaos. More important, however, is my own belief that the origin and practice of art have so much in common with science that they justify at least a few words.

The arts, as we know them, derive obviously from craftsmanship. The artist follows the craftsman in fashioning with his hands things which other people desire but which they have not the skill to make for themselves, and this has always been his function. Art is necessarily an activity of individuals freed from the necessity of finding or producing their own needs of food and shelter, and it can only develop where there is a defined social structure by which one man, who desires what the artist can produce, can ensure that less-gifted men do the work that provides the artist's food and shelter and gives him leisure to exercise his skill.

There is a real pleasure in developing skill in any sort of craftsmanship. For one thing, the work is physically easier when skill has been acquired; for another, the product of the skilled man is more effective for its purpose and it is more highly desired. This automatically raises his level in the dominance-order amongst his fellow craftsmen, always the most potent of incentives to achievement.

For the same reasons, there will always be a tendency for the very skilful man to produce something beyond that originally desired by his patron. If a man asks for a sword from his smith, he will be content with a properly balanced and tempered blade, but he will be pleased if the hilt is ornamented in some acceptable fashion. It is to the craftsman's major interest if he can elaborate his product in such a way that the result is desirable and can only be produced by him. The dominance characteristics of human beings are such that the highest value is attached to the feeling that 'I alone can order this man to do such and such', and only slightly lower value to 'I alone can do such and such'. Throughout history, the artist-craftsman has had to steer his course between, on the one hand, producing just what all his contemporaries could produce and, on the other, introducing changes which only he could execute but which went beyond what his patrons, conditioned by traditional tastes, were willing to tolerate.

A superficial acquaintance with the history of painting suggests that, basically, it represents a continuous elaboration of technique in ways which will exploit the individuality of the artist and yet which never introduce too abrupt a break with the current tradition of the art. The change in the character of painting and sculpture in the last hundred years with the almost total deviation from accurate representation of the object seems to be, from our present point of view, a simple acceleration of the process by which each significant artist must introduce some novelty, some individuality into his work if it is to be desired by his patrons. It is significant that once an artist has developed his characteristic style, he almost always continues to produce works which in subject matter and style are easily recognizable as *his*. He has created for himself a dominance-order in which he is supreme, without a rival. Real greatness can allow a modern artist to go beyond this. Sometimes a genius like Picasso can initiate a whole series of new approaches and be hailed as Number One in each.

Of all the difficulties of today's world, the most intractable may prove to be the intrinsic momentum of technology. Over the last two hundred years this has built up progressively and each year the process seems to accelerate. Momentum in physics is the product of mass by velocity and, by 1970, the sheer mass of science-based industry and the velocity of change have combined to produce a frightening situation.

In the United States, a population of 200 million people can produce enough of the goods and services that are desired to allow each individual to consume what is conventionally costed at $3,000 per annum. This is, nominally at least, more than thirty times what is available per head in heavily-populated under-developed countries like India and Pakistan. The process within the affluent country has become almost automatically self-expanding, the gross national product showing a real increase corrected for changing prices of 3 or 4 per cent per annum for the established countries, from 6 to 9 per cent for countries on the way up, West Germany, Israel and Japan.

From the particular point of view of this discussion the significant features of the affluent society are:

1 Either spontaneously, or under the stimulus of advertisement and status-seeking, all people desire more goods and services than they are in a position to obtain. Of course there are exceptions, but they are insignificant in relation to general trends.

2 Competition for profit, plus the existence of managers, technologists and industrial scientists eager to gain prestige within the field of their skills, will ensure a steady increase in the desirability of the product and, less regularly, a reduction in its cost.

3 The production of food can now be done by from 5 to 10 per cent of the population, as contrasted with 50 per cent in the United States in 1900 and close to 100 per cent in primitive subsistence communities.

4 In secondary industry, automation will progressively reduce the man-power needed to produce a given quota of goods. There will, however, be an increasing demand for the limited supply of highly trained, highly intelligent designers, technologists and managers, and for qualified technicians. Individuals of low IQ will be needed in diminishing numbers.

5 An increasing proportion of the population will need to be occupied in tertiary industry. Prolonged education and earlier retirement will also be unavoidable.

6 If waste of national effort in war and preparation for war could be eliminated, the current trend would be greatly accelerated.

It is difficult to see how any of these tendencies can be reversed or controlled in the context of a competitive industrial system and a democratic basis of political power. Nor does it seem likely that

a very different result will emerge from the natural development
of socialist States like the USSR. One of the most significant factors in any type of industrial country that can maintain political
independence must be the existence and characteristic behaviour
of the highly skilled. Probably correctly, every country of any
size considers that it must have the capacity to produce modern
weapons of war. To do so, it must have the same technological
and industrial capacity as any of its assumed rivals. In effect, this
means that every country, no matter what social philosophy it
claims, must have a relatively large and dominant group of technologists and managers and an effective system of scientific and
technical education. Men with the skills needed to design aircraft
or computers, or to switch a factory to the production of a new
design, and who have the responsibility for the 'goodness' of the
product are eager for professional status and prestige. Politicians
may regard it as a matter of political survival that a weapon
should be as good as or superior to anything that the Americans
possess, but unless all my knowledge of human nature is wrong,
the designer or design-team responsible for the weapon will be
more concerned with *their* success in producing a better bomb
and the rewards in status, salary and applause that go with it.

The same attitude will be just as evident in the civil industry
of a socialist country as in a competitive economy. As long as
technologists have ideas and opportunities to test them, the
quality, convenience of use and cheapness of goods—or any other
aspects that make them desirable—will go on improving. Improvement, of course, is in terms of short-term desirability. It has
nothing necessarily to do with what is in the interests of the community as a whole. The average American likes a big powerful
car with air-conditioning, power-steering, and the rest. It weighs
two tons, uses a great deal of fuel and over-crowds roads as fast
as they can be built or widened. Road deaths and serious accidents, which depend mainly on the density of cars on the roads
and the average driving-speed, have become increasingly frequent
in all countries. They have a mortality which includes as many
young men as are killed per annum in a large 'conventional' war,
and road casualty victims make up the largest component of

hospital-bed occupancy in most advanced countries. It is reasonably certain that good public transport and small electric cars of limited speed and range for city use would unchoke the cities and greatly reduce road casualties. In Australia, any such move waits on what happens overseas. In the meantime, more and more cars of greater average weight, horsepower and speed are being sold.

The automatic tendency for progress engendered by technological competition for achievement and prestige is very evident in the civil aviation industry at the present time. Supersonic military aircraft are presumably a necessary result of the ghastly logic of modern weaponry. To build a technically sound and commercially profitable supersonic transport for civil use is a technical challenge to the designers, and with a few hundreds of millions of dollars made available by government it becomes an exhilarating task for the whole team. In any other sense, the whole project is absurd. Sonic boom will be an intolerable nuisance to every community not powerful enough to veto passage of aircraft at supersonic speeds in their vicinity. The only advantage claimed is that it will take a business-man or a politician on an intercontinental trip in a few hours' less time than the present jets. When one thinks of the current delays in the city-to-airport, airport-to-city stages of any air journey and the disorganization of one's 'biological clock' by any long journey with a significant east-west component, the gain of those few hours seems a ludicrously small return. The benefit to the tiny fraction of the population that will use the supersonics will be heavily outweighed by the discomfort of the booms to vastly larger numbers of people. Yet nothing can apparently prevent an international competition in futility, now that Nixon has given the go-ahead for the American SST.

The supersonic civil transport is only one of the examples where an irrational technological and scientific momentum is generated on the basis that because a difficult or spectacular thing can be done, it must be done. It is the equivalent at the scientific and technological level of the famous answer as to why one should climb Everest—because it is there.

The worst offences have naturally been in relation to nuclear energy. Any sane man with a knowledge of ecology and the processes of evolution should have known from the beginning that tampering with nuclear energy, either for explosions in war or power development in peace, would be fatal to the integrity of living process. Sooner or later the bombs will be used. There have been minor accidents in nuclear reactors already and, if one can judge from the refusal of insurance companies to handle such business, knowledgeable men expect that a major catastrophe is a statistical certainty in the long run. Judging from what has been published, the safety record of both military and civil nuclear industry has been extraordinarily good, but the difficulties will increase as power reactors multiply and the problem of safely disposing of large amounts of radio-active debris may tempt some to use dangerous short cuts.

The contemporary Mount Everest of technology is the search for the production of industrial power by controlled nuclear-fusion reactions. One gathers that there are still doubts whether it is possible in principle even to design a 'reaction vessel' within which the necessary physical conditions can be generated. It was once said to be a clean reaction, but in the last semi-popular discussion of the most likely type of reaction to be used, it was stated that the highly toxic H3 tritium isotope would be found very difficult to prevent escaping into the environment in unacceptable amounts.

The current developments in nuclear armaments in both America and Russia provide the outstanding example of technological momentum gone insane. Mutual deterrence with 'overkill' capacity is now to be elaborated with ABM's and MIRVs, but these can wait for discussion in a later chapter.

At the present time, West Germany, Holland and the United Kingdom, in an attempt to break American monopoly in the production of enriched uranium, are developing gas centrifuge methods to enrich the content of U235. If successful, this may become the road to the 'poor man's' hydrogen bomb, the most likely of all the possible triggers for the apocalypse.

In the field of super poisons, there are still some scientific challenges which, accepted simply to advance knowledge, could lead to things worse than the nerve gases. Botulinus toxin, the most poisonous substance known, is a simple protein composed only of amino acids. Presumably only a small part of the molecule carries its toxicity, and I should be surprised if experimental stock piles of the active small molecule are not already in existence. There are hints of even more lethal toxic proteins in the stinging cells of coelenterates, such as the Australian sea-wasp (*Chironex fleckeri*).

A few years ago, I created a certain stir by claiming that the only practical implication of current work on viral genetics, with the elucidation of the genetic code and rapid advances in 'sequencing' nucleic acids, was likely to be the production, probably by accident rather than by design, of dangerously virulent unnatural variants of polio and other RNA viruses. Perhaps none of these biological examples of dangerous technological momentum are of much importance as potential weapons of war, but if any régime found it necessary or expedient to cultivate assassination by methods not recognizable as murder, molecular biology could become very important.

In all this, I am only saying what is being said increasingly by scientists and other people of insight and goodwill, that the scientist must be prepared to look at the social consequences of each scientific discovery. One might go further and say that, both in the competition for better weapons and in competition for profit, there are potentialities—or certainties?—that may destroy civilization.

DEATH AND
six THE BURDEN
OF GENES

As I have told, I was trained in medicine and in medical micro-biology. Apart from a year as a hospital intern and a month or two as a ship's surgeon, I have never practised medicine, but I have never been wholly outside of the medical environment and I have always been deeply interested in the more general and philosophical aspects of human disease, ageing and death.

I have written a good deal about the relationship of medical research in the laboratories to the practical needs of medical care and I am rather unpopular with the present generation of labora-tory research men in Australia as a result. There are very few aspects of human affairs about which one cannot say that change has been faster and more far-reaching in the last fifty years than ever before. It certainly holds for medical science, and a year ago I tried to illustrate this by writing an autobiographical account of my own sense of the changes in medicine and biology under the title of *Changing Patterns*.

Perhaps the pattern is even now accelerating its rate of change, and, like so much else in the world, there is a great gulf between the state of medicine and the patterns for its future as seen in the affluent countries and the poverty-stricken half of mankind. I have clear, perhaps too clear ideas on what is needed at the medical level for the world in 1970. There are just two things:

The first is to provide the whole world with the level of pre-ventive and curative medicine that was available to affluent countries about 1955.

The second is to establish population control in every country in the world.

The rest is trivial and, at the risk of being branded as an atheist in the College of Cardinals, I doubt whether more than one per cent of the medical research now being done has any real bearing on what the world needs. It is still worth doing, but it is not being done, as we used to think forty years ago, for the good of mankind. In a book on human biology, I believe that one of the important things to be discussed is the influence of medical science and of care and compassion for the unfortunate on the present and future state of the human species.

Animals in the wild state are healthy except under completely unusual circumstances. If they become sick, they will be taken by predators; if they are born genetically deformed or otherwise handicapped, they die soon and have no offspring. Nevertheless, no animal population is genetically uniform. Mutation, usually in unimportant corners of the genetic system, is occurring perhaps once or twice in the germ cells of every individual, and every bird in a flock of starlings, every fish in a school of sardines differs in some genetic detail from any other. The chief basis for that statement depends on research by Dobshansky and others on the genetic composition of wild populations of fruit-flies, but there is no reason to believe that it does not also hold for more familiar species. What is important to grasp is that most genetic differences are recessive, that is, not expressed if the other member of the pair of genes concerned is normal, or in some other way neutralized so that they produce no significant change in the likelihood of survival in Nature. If, by the chances of the 'shuffle of the cards', when genes from male and female parents produce the new combination which determines the genetic structure of the offspring, two 'bad' genes come together and the young one is handicapped by the result, Nature will see to it that the weakling is struck down by one or other impact of the environment before it breeds.

It is a commonplace that for every species of animal many more young are born than will survive to reproductive age. Death is by the attack of predators, by inclement weather, by parasitic or infectious disease, and rarely by poisoning or starvation. In almost every case it is the death of a genetically healthy organism under some impact from the environment. For the first million years of his history as the genus *Homo*, man was in the same position and for human beings everywhere this held virtually to the beginning of the twentieth century. The great majority of deaths occurred in infants and children and only a small proportion of people survived to die at ages over sixty-five. Everywhere the main cause of death was infectious disease, the nature of which varied with country and climate. Faulty feeding, particularly of infants at weaning, was another prime cause. Accident, homicide, war and famine played their part. As in wild animals, most of the individuals who died were genetically healthy enough. Children with manifest inherited abnormalities were born, but most did not survive long.

The great health achievement of the last one hundred and fifty years has been the gradual build-up of our capacity, in one way or another, to allow the genetically sound child to avoid or surmount the impacts of the environment that in earlier times would have killed him. In an earlier chapter, I have mentioned how the world population began to increase at a slowly rising tempo in the seventeenth and eighteenth centuries, and how the rate accelerated in the nineteenth century.

There is nothing to suggest that medical science or medical care had any direct influence on population levels until well into the twentieth century. More children survived in England because farm yields were improved in the seventeenth century, canal-building on a large scale brought food more regularly to the growing cities and, in the nineteenth century, food from the open lands overseas further improved the level of nutrition. Populations grew rapidly in the predominantly rural populations of overseas colonies. There is a credible statement that, judging from the distribution of family names amongst the Afrikaans people of South Africa, many of the Dutch founding-fathers of the sixteenth century averaged some 12,500 direct descendants by 1960. This is basically a commentary on the unhealthiness of the European urban environment in the intervening centuries.

The important change in that environment was begun in the

middle years of the nineteenth century, with the first active measures to improve the health of city-dwellers. It was self-evident that children died excessively in the poorest, dirtiest and smelliest parts of London. In the days before bacteriology, it was not unreasonable to assume that disease might be caused by foul smelling air and that human faeces as the source of the foulest smells should be eliminated from the environment by adequate sewage disposal. There was growing evidence, too, that cholera and what we know now as typhoid fever were in some way related to the use of water, which was or could have been contaminated with human excreta. Good drains and a clean water-supply were having a major effect on urban health well before anything was known of the bacteriology of cholera or typhoid fever. Any improvement in the level of nutrition, in household cleanliness and in personal cleanliness and good manners, diminished the incidence and mortality from infectious disease. All were manifestations of a rising standard of living. Medical care also improved, but there is no reason to believe that, as such, it had any effect on the mortality from gastroenteritis, scarlet fever or diphtheria.

One of the most interesting features of the history of medicine is the course of deaths from pulmonary tuberculosis from 1850 onward. It fell slowly but steadily from then until 1950. Then, with the widespread use of potent chemotherapy, there was a great acceleration of the fall in mortality. Despite all the stress on sanatorium treatment, artificial pneumothorax and the rest in the 1930s and '40s, most would, I think, now agree that treatment, as such, had no influence on tuberculous mortality until 1950. Once an effective treatment had been discovered, its results were immediately apparent. The slow improvement over the previous one hundred years was no more than a reflection of a rising standard of living.

It is probable that the first real influence of measures specifically based on medical science began soon after the First World War. It is more than probable that in the armies of that war many lives were saved by improved surgical techniques and a significant number by the use of anti-tetanus serum. The

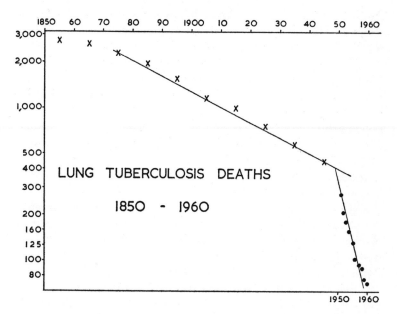

Fig. 5 The course of preventive medicine: deaths from lung tuberculosis in England and Wales, 1850–1960. The first phase, 1850–1950, illustrates the effect of a steadily rising standard of living, probably without any significant contribution from medical treatment. With the introduction of streptomycin and other anti-tuberculosis drugs, 1946–50, the picture changes dramatically.

effectiveness of the current typhoid vaccines, widely claimed at the time, is open to doubt. During the 1920s, however, insulin for the treatment of diabetes and immunization against diphtheria were introduced and widely adopted. They provided the first evidence clearly visible in national statistics that medical action, as such, was saving lives. Then the flood-gates of discovery began to open—the first synthetic anti-malarials, atebrine and plasmaquine came in 1932–33, prontosil and the later sulpha drugs appeared from 1935 onwards with their first outstanding success against puerperal fever. Penicillin, the greatest life-saver of them all, had been discovered in 1929, but it was high-priority wartime research in England and America that made it available to medicine. The other antibiotics followed swiftly, of which only streptomycin, because of its action against tuberculosis, need be mentioned. In 1943, the power of DDT as an insecticide to stop a typhus epidemic in its tracks was demonstrated in Naples and there was new hope against every insect-borne disease that plagued man or domestic animal. Finally, and passing over many lesser achievements, came the success of the Salk vaccine against poliomyelitis in 1954.

During the 1939–45 war, the treatment of wounds was revolutionized by the use of blood transfusion, the sulphonamides and, in the later stages, penicillin. Surgical procedures were standardized and immense advances made in methods of rehabilitating the disabled. Two indirect results of great significance for tropical under-developed countries were, first, the effective treatment of cholera by the administration of appropriate fluids into the blood circulation and the development of simple but effective field-latrines and other types of 'environmental sanitation'.

Research on human nutrition was active from the very beginning of the twentieth century, but its fruits were not fully visible till the Second World War. It is one of the paradoxes of human affairs that it required grave food shortages and strict rationing to give England well-nourished children in all social classes for the first time in its history.

I tend to name 1955, the year when the efficacy of poliomyelitis vaccine was finally established, as the end of the epoch in which disease and disability, due to the impact of the environment, was effectively controlled. Except for unlucky individuals, often with genetic weaknesses, virtually all potentially lethal infectious diseases could be prevented or cured by means available in all affluent countries. Trauma that did not involve massive damage to vital organs could nearly always be handled effectively if the injured person could reach a standard resuscitation unit while he was still alive. Malnutrition and gross nutritional disease like scurvy, rickets and pellagra are virtually unknown, even in the poorest groups of countries like America and Australia.

Success in this handling of the environmental causes of disease and disability has been the greatest of all human achievements and has given an atmosphere of prestige and promise to medical research which has persisted to the present. I believe, and have frequently stated in public, that in fact there is a very important difference between the pattern of medical research between 1930 and 1955 and the character of contemporary medical research at the end of the 1960s. It is important for an understanding of the human situation to define the differences and to show how success on the earlier scale cannot now be even dreamt of.

Any general statement must be somewhat over-simplified, but, with that qualification, the following may be an acceptable summary of the medical situation in regard to diseases arising from *environmental* causes:

1   Diseases and disabilities due to the impact of the environment in general affect people without regard to their genetic make-up.

2   The nature of the impact can be defined in scientific terms, pathogenic micro-organisms can be isolated, identified and tested for their susceptibility to antibiotics, physically damaging agents can be defined and measured by physical techniques, the necessary constituents of a diet and possible poisons can be assessed by the methods of the chemical laboratory.

3   With only minor differences, the effect of agents which cause disease in man is basically similar in the mammals which are available for laboratory study. A preventive or therapeutic manipulation which is successful in an experimental animal has usually been applicable in principle to man, and in most cases has proved to be successful when it is intelligently applied to the human problem.

The situation is very different when we approach the human disabilities which are not due to the impact of a definable environmental agent. Some are known to be due to genetic anomalies, with a range from trivial disabilities, like a tendency to freckles or minor refraction errors of the eye, to gross conditions, of which four relatively well-known ones may be mentioned. *Haemophilia*, in which the patient bleeds uncontrollably after slight injury, and *agammaglobulinaemia*, where the patient cannot produce antibody to deal with infections, are both 'sex-linked recessives' affecting only males. In *albinism* the child is born without pigment in skin, hair or eyes, and in *phenylketonuria* there is a chemical abnormality which produces gross mental deficiency. These may affect either boys or girls. A second group includes what are called the somatic genetic diseases in which abnormal genetic changes occur only in some cells of the body. In genetic disease proper, the changes are potentially present in every cell. The somatic genetic disabilities include a variety of local anomalies, like moles and birth-marks, diseases of the blood, like leukaemia, and a wide variety of more or less related conditions, of which Hodgkin's disease is the only one that a layman is likely to have heard of. Benign tumours, like the common fibroids of the uterus and most or all malignant cancers, are derived from genetic anomalies involving a single initial cell from which an enormous and over-active 'clone' of descendant cells has developed. There is a group of diseases, the 'autoimmune diseases', including amongst others, rheumatoid arthritis and pernicious anaemia, which may also have a somatic genetic origin. I have argued strongly in favour of such a view, but probably a majority of pathologists are still unconvinced.

The third group are the so-called degenerative diseases of old age, notably cardio-vascular disease. All of these undoubtedly contain genetic and somatic genetic components. Personally, I would accept the point of view expressed by Alex Comfort, that ageing is essentially a loss of interest by Nature in organisms which, having ended their reproductive responsibilities, are no longer subject to evolutionary pressure. Once a man or woman has raised a family to adulthood, anything that happens to either is of no biological concern to the human species. Those of us over sixty are 'on our own'—control and reparative mechanisms go on functioning but they lack the self-renewing quality of youth. Somatic mutations lead to enzyme defects, somewhere or other there is a functional break-down with repercussions elsewhere in 'the works', with a variable but inexorable movement towards decrepitude and increasing vulnerability to environmental insult.

Death is a biological necessity, but it is a word which must hardly be mentioned in its full personal impact. No discussion of the intrinsic causes of disease and what can or should be done about them can be meaningful unless the fact of death and the evolutionary significance of death can be looked at squarely. One thing should be said at once. The concept of any sort of conscious experience after death is biologically inadmissible. Being dead has the same relation to conscious life as the state of not yet being born. Thought, consciousness, words, the sensory input, the motor output and all that goes between, are wholly dependent on the disposition and correct metabolic function of our nerve cells. When a man dies his universe ends with him. Dying is something which, for good evolutionary reasons, we fear and struggle against—but death, as such, is another matter. Many of us have thought how nice it would be to go happily to sleep one night and not wake up!

All societies have had curious irrationalities and ambiguities about death, our own not least. Every healthy pair of adolescents, one male, one female, could physiologically produce from fourteen to twenty children. In every civilized country the average is between two and four, so the vast majority of couples deny life to a dozen or more human beings. Nobody, not even the Pope, raises a serious voice against this. Abortion is another matter: hairs have been split as to when the soul enters the body of the foetus, and logic has always been muddied by that other evolutionary need, that from the moment of birth an infant must provoke affection and protection primarily of the mother, but, by extension, to the father, and, in diluted form, to virtually all normal human beings. Logically, it is no more anti-social to eliminate painlessly a foetus or infant before the development of any form of conceptual insight than it is to deny birth to the full complement of children of which each individual is capable.

It is still taboo to base any action on such logic, just as it is for a doctor to offer euthanasia to a patient in intolerable pain. Here, however, the taboo is less universal than that which protects infants with gross genetic abnormalities, like spina bifida, against a painless exemption from the misery of life. Not every physician feels that he needs to 'strive officiously to keep alive' the cancer patient for whom continued life is a painful burden.

On the other side of the coin, we seem to be equally illogical. In Australia, we expose young men to a double lottery to decide which of them will die in a manifestly futile war. We put no impediment in the way of young men buying motor-cycles, which is an entry into a lottery for death of about the same probability and the same futility as conscription for Vietnam.

We are beginning to develop common sense about sex and birth control. A similar replacement of taboos and hysteria about death may come in similar fashion: it is equally needed.

All this discussion of contemporary attitudes toward death is peripheral to the primary problem of how medical science is to handle the intrinsic causes of disease and genetic inadequacy.

I am frankly pessimistic about the relevance of research, in the ordinary sense, to the prevention or treatment of human disease of intrinsic origin. The primary difficulty is the complete absence of any immediately relevant laboratory models. The key word is relevant. The whole exciting world of molecular biology, the biochemical basis for genetics, was worked out on the model provided by a common type of bacterium and the bacterial viruses which parasitize it. So far there has not been a single application of molecular biology to the prevention or treatment of disease in man or domestic animals. All laboratory animals grow old and die, they frequently develop cancer and sometimes suffer from genetic disease of various types. Mice have a short life-span; there are many pure lines available, enormous numbers are under study and, as would be expected, most types of intrinsic disease have been recognized in mice and extensively studied. I believe that I have a reasonably comprehensive knowledge of such studies. Again, I feel justified in saying that nothing learnt from such studies has yet had any bearing on prevention or treatment of intrinsic disease in man. Most laboratory-workers accept their impotence to handle intrinsic causes—but their usual escape from the difficulty is to explore possibilities, however remote, that what we call intrinsic diseases are in fact due to extrinsic agents.

Viruses, particularly 'slow viruses', are being implicated as causes for cancer, autoimmune disease and a variety of degenerative conditions of the brain. So far, no unequivocal examples are on record.

In the absence of laboratory models, studies of human disease due to genetic and degenerative processes have had to be in the form of clinical research. There have been many fascinating studies, but apart from providing some useful rules for 'genetic counselling' in relation to gross single gene abnormalities, there is again nothing of practical importance. There is, however, one genetic disease of man, phenylketonuria ('PKU'), for which heavily publicized claims for its effective control have been made. As a result, it has been intensively studied in the last five or ten years and a second generation of critical and balanced reports are now available for discussion. I believe that it gives a fair picture of the virtual impossibility of handling genetic disease and is therefore worth analysing at some length.

PKU was recognized as a result of the discovery that the urine of a certain proportion of mentally deficient children gave a positive reaction for an unusual type of metabolic product—a phenyl ketone. Sometimes two or more of such children came from the same family and the condition had all the signs of a genetic disease, an 'inborn error of metabolism'. The first recognition of such inborn errors was by an English physician, Sir Archibald Garrod, but their full understanding had to wait until genetic methods were applied in microbiology.

As a result of work begun about 1942 by Beadle and Tatum, ways of handling fungi and bacteria were developed by which their genetic capacity to carry out the various requirements of living chemistry could be studied. A famous generalization, 'One gene, one enzyme', emerged from this work and with some minor qualifications it holds today. If, for proper reasons, a chemical compound A must be converted into another compound D in a living organism, it is usual to find that it is done in a series of steps:

$$A \xrightarrow{x} B \xrightarrow{y} C \xrightarrow{z} D.$$

Each arrow represents the action of an enzyme x, y or z, according to its special function. Each enzyme is controlled by a gene, a unit of the genetic mechanism of the cell. Gene x can be defined as the gene which allows enzyme x to be made, and so on. If in our hypothetical series, gene y, responsible for the B → C change, is lost or damaged by mutation, then enzyme y will not function. Enzyme x will go on making B, and B will accumulate in much larger amounts than it should, since there is no enzyme to turn it into C, and since no more C is being made, there is no precursor for D.

In human beings, things are considerably more complex than in any micro-organism, but the 'one gene, one enzyme' law probably still holds true. Phenyl-alanine, which it will simplify things to call PA, is one of the amino acid building-blocks that make up protein. It cannot be synthesized in the body from anything simpler, so that a certain amount of PA in the diet is essential for human nutrition. It is present in nearly all food proteins, and when their digestion is completed the PA circulates in the blood. Like other amino acids it needs to be broken down for some of the body's uses by enzymes, at least two of which are relevant to PKU. Absence of one enzyme, A, allows PA to accumulate in the blood and in the presence of the other, B, the excess of PA is converted into the derivative, the phenyl ketone, which gives the positive urine test by which we recognize that something is wrong.

Most cases of PKU are such because enzyme A is missing as a result of the individual's possessing two faulty genes at the same place on the same chromosome. The fault in the gene is what we call recessive. If, in that particular situation, there is one normal and one faulty gene the child is normal. Only when there are two faulty genes does the enzyme fail to develop. Anyone with a smattering of elementary genetics knows that if two individuals, both of whom have one normal and one faulty gene, marry they will have about one child in four who suffers from the disease. It is almost a matter of simple algebra:

$$N\text{-}F \times N\text{-}F = 1N\text{-}N + 2N\text{-}F + 1F\text{-}F$$

only the one F-F being affected by disease.

In the child with the F-F formula, PA accumulates in the blood. In small amounts, PA is harmless and even in relatively large amounts it could be excreted in the phenyl-ketone form into the urine with no more than a trivial effect on most organs of the body. The all-important exception is that, for reasons not clearly understood, the presence of abnormally large amounts of phenyl-alanine disrupts the proper development of brain and mind after birth. The children develop as low-grade mental defectives. A considerable proportion, but not all the infants, who are found to give a positive PK test soon after birth, belong to this category of typical PKU, and for the present we can assume that all PKU depends on this mechanism.

There are clearly several ways in principle of 'curing' PKU: (1) We might replace the bad gene by a good gene in all cells of the body. (2) We could graft a big enough mass of tissue from a normal person, the liver perhaps, to supply an adequate amount of enzyme A for the whole body. Neither of these is remotely practicable, and there is no suggestion that any practical technique could be devised in the foreseeable future. (3) We could provide a diet containing very little phenyl-alanine and feed this, for as long as necessary, to any children giving a positive PK test at or soon after birth. This has been the accepted and orthodox approach for about the last five or six years. (4) A socially inadmissible but logical solution is infanticide, a painless and dignified disposal of the tiny proportion of babies with the typical urine reaction. A suggestion that might make this more socially acceptable is to develop a test on the foetal fluids before birth so that to dispose of the offspring could be called abortion rather than infanticide. (5) Finally, there is another logical and socially acceptable approach. This is to ensure that no fertile matings occur between people whose genetic constitution is such that they can have a PKU baby. If there is one PKU baby, there is a 1:4 chance that any other child born to the same parents will also be a PKU. If there were a way of being sure whether a person apparently normal was a carrier of one PKU gene neutralized by one corresponding normal gene (a heterozygote in technical terms), or had both genes normal (a normal homozygote), we

could ensure no more PKU babies by arranging that any heterozygote married only a person who could be certified as normally
homozygous for that particular gene. As this normal group con-
tains more than 99 per cent of possible mates, very little hardship
would be involved. The only difficulty is that refined cellular
chemistry will be needed if the differentiation is to be made. It
is likely that a method will be found, but this is not yet certain
and it could well turn out to be socially impossible to apply it.
To be effective, every person in the community would have to be
tested, around the age of fifteen, for this and perhaps other
potential genetic abnormalities. All would be extremely rare, and
unless the test were of the simplest possible character, the
amount of skilled labour required would be disproportionate to
the possible benefit.

So far, treatment by feeding a low PKU diet is the only practical approach. Unfortunately, it is a very difficult matter to
provide all the necessary components of protein and eliminate
the phenyl-alanine or, rather, since it is itself necessary for many
functions, to give just the amount which will fulfil necessary functions but not allow it to accumulate in damaging amount. To the
best of my knowledge, the results are still equivocal. Some appear
to do well, but there are many quite unsatisfactory results.

As is the way of biological discoveries, the condition has turned
out to be much more complex than at first thought. There is now
evidence that some PKUs show no mental deficiency, even on a
normal diet, and there are some who respond very little to the
special low phenyl-alanine diet. Finally, if the treated child had
too little phenyl-alanine circulating in the blood, the mental condition deteriorates in much the same fashion as in severe protein
deficiency. The PKU baby obviously includes a variety of genetic
conditions and, as yet, there is no clear teaching on how best to
handle them. The 'orthodox' treatment is obviously not the full
answer.

It has yet to be shown, even for 'typical' PKU, that children so
treated can reach the intelligence that their inheritance and home
environment should allow, nor is it known how long the very
unnatural diet must be maintained.

That is an attempt to present a completely objective approach to the only genetic disease for which biochemical means of recognition and treatment have been applied on an extensive scale. I have stressed the unsatisfactory nature of our knowledge of the complex genetic conditions concerned, the danger of the treatment to the children, and the very dubious nature of the benefit received. To the best of my knowledge, very similar complexities and much greater difficulties in the way of possible treatment apply to dozens of other genetic abnormalities, mostly, like PKU, albinism and cystic fibrosis, rare conditions, 'double recessives' which condemn children to idiocy, disfigurement, constant invalidism or early death. It is clear that medical research can do very little here that can lighten the human burdens.

The second great assemblage of human ills which arise from intrinsic causes comprises the diseases due to somatic mutation, of which only the most important, cancer, need be discussed in a non-technical book. Cancer, according to the view which seems to me self-evident, arises because amongst the errors which may happen in the genetic mechanisms of body cells, there is one particular group, and only one, which will bring the existence of a somatic mutation to the individual's or to his doctor's notice. This is when a cell is so changed that it and its descendants are forced to go on multiplying without regard to the controlling forces which, as it were, keep the body in shape. Cells are very tiny; hundreds of thousands are going wrong every day of our lives, they die or stop functioning properly and the millions of still normal cells just go on behaving normally. The abnormal ones have no recognizable effect. A wrong sort of cell can only have a visible effect if, by repeated multiplication, it builds up a clone of some millions. The commonest way this happens is in the appearance of a tumour, benign like a uterine fibroid, or malignant like cancer of the lung.

Not everybody accepts that cancer comes from within. Many pathologists believe that all cancers are produced by viruses, all of us are aware that exposure to toxic substances like tar or cigarette smoke can greatly increase the likelihood of cancer of certain types. I have written much at the technical level to say why I am wholly unimpressed by the virus theory, but no such discussion is relevant here. The brutal fact is that nothing derived from the virus theory of cancer has any bearing on the treatment or diagnosis of human cancer. The whole of its treatment is based on the assumption that cancer cells are body cells which have broken away from control, but in most essential respects are still human cells. They have been changed genetically from the normal cell from which a given cancer arose and there is no conceivable way of reversing that change. Just as the stock-breeder culls every animal with any hereditary defect, so the only objective of the surgeon and radiologist is to cut out with the knife or cautery, or selectively destroy with X-rays, all the cancer cells and as few as possible of normal cells. Experience and clinical research has steadily improved the results of cancer treatment, but it has been an empirical process hardly affected at all by laboratory research on tumours of mice or other animals.

There is no possibility, in my opinion, that a synthetic drug capable of killing cancer cells but not normal cells will ever be found. The only hope of selective killing is related to the fact that the body, if it is grafted with a piece of skin from someone else, will destroy that skin without damaging its own. Cancer cells are to a significant degree foreign to the body and we are beginning to believe that many incipient cancers may start to develop and be nipped in the bud by immune cells before there is any clinical sign of cancer. A manifest cancer, on this view, is due to the failure in this instance of the mechanism we speak of as immunological surveillance. Experiments in animals suggest that if we knew that a cancer was beginning to develop in someone's lung there is a possibility, in principle, that we could help the body to get rid of it. Unfortunately, the first set of requirements seems likely always to be impossible. Every cancer differs from every other cancer, so the first thing necessary is to recognize that there is an early cancer and procure some of the cells that compose it without damage to the patient. Neither seems to be possible in any foreseeable future. If we had those cells, the procedure would be to let them proliferate in tissue culture and render them harmless, though still nominally alive, probably by

X-ray treatment, to make a type of vaccine. By injecting an appropriate dose of this we might stimulate the body sufficiently to produce enough immune cells to defeat a cancer that would otherwise have got the upper hand. An immune cell of the patient himself, specifically active against the cancer cell involved, is the only magic bullet which can be trusted to kill the cancer cell without also doing grave damage to normal cells. One cannot make vaccines that might influence incipient human cancer from animal cancer cells nor, for the matter of that, from a developed cancer in some other patient.

The obstacle is simply the enormous complexity of human cells and the great variety of changes that can be associated with cancer. In a very literal sense, every cancer is as individual from every other cancer as the patient is from every other human being. Science can be concerned only with reproducible situations and medical science is almost restricted to situations which can be reproduced in all essentials in experimental animals. The individual condition in an individual patient can be dealt with only by the patient himself. If that fails, and the cancer becomes clinically evident, it can only be dealt with by attempting empirically to excise or destroy the malignant cells. Perhaps it should be added that there are some optimists amongst immunologists who point out another possibility. It is very easy to use drugs of several types to diminish the effectiveness of an immune response, such as we believe to play a part in protection against cancer. Occasionally, but never in wholly convincing fashion, immunologists have claimed that some treatment of an experimental animal has allowed an overall improvement in immune responses irrespective of what sort of virus or vaccine that was being used for immunization. Without any conviction, whatever, I wonder sometimes whether in one hundred years' time people over sixty will have pellets of natural or synthetic hormones implanted under their skin designed to keep their immune responses youthful enough to knock out incipient cancers. Let me repeat that this is only a pipe dream!

Men will continue to fear death and to ask for extension of life for themselves, or for others, without much regard to the quality of that life. For the foreseeable future, the law will frown on any deliberate deviation from that pattern. Anyone with a medical background will know that, apart from what I have called disabilities due to the impact of the environment, no disease or disability can be handled in wholly satisfactory fashion. Each of us does the best we can within the limitations of our knowledge, of the facilities available, and of the personality of the patient. Whatever is done could, in principle, be done better. One can foresee a never-ending effort to improve results, and probably until the end of time whenever an intelligent and enthusiastic team of clinical scientists set out to improve the handling of some disability that interests them, they are almost bound to do so. Whether their improvements can be made equally successful in other hands or in other countries will be less predictable, but, overall, progress will continue. Survival and cure are not the only things that a patient requires. Freedom from pain, from discomfort and from personal indignity during the course of illness are equally desired and not always adequately provided. Even more liable to be lacking is the patient's sense of being affectionately cared for by somebody.

In one way or another, medical care will go on improving and it probably matters little if the laboratories of the biological sciences that now cluster around the medical schools provide less and less of what is directly relevant to preventive and curative medicine. Progressively, they will find other functions to fulfil in the hyper-affluent society of the future.

seven

ETHICS
OF A
BIOLOGIST

Here, as at many other points in writing this book, I find myself
having to ask whether what I am undertaking is almost indecently
beyond anyone's capacity. To start to write about the modern
ethical approach, to compress what is relevant in regard to
values and morals into twenty pages, seems to be in arrogant
disregard of what has interested and puzzled every philosopher,
every literate individual almost, since civilization began. There
is only one justification that can be claimed, but I believe that it
is a cogent one. Every man must judge his own behaviour by his
own sense of values, irrespective of how much or how little he
knows of what Plato or Macchiavelli or Bertrand Russell have
thought and written. He cannot avoid accepting that personal
responsibility and if he is to be honest in writing about what he
thinks to be important, he must state his ethical position. Each
man's set of values will be influenced by temperament and experience, but all start with the same questions. What are the
values that can be used as a conscious guide to human behaviour?
What is good? What is true? What is beautiful?

As a scientist, I think I can answer the third of those questions
only. Truth in science, and in other fields of scholarship, is that
complex of recorded observations, generalizations and theories
which in the opinion of competent scholars has not yet been
proved to be wrong. Truth must always be provisional, which
does not prevent it coming ever closer to certainty for a great
range of knowledge. Scientists from any country, capitalist or
communist, would probably accept that definition of truth.

Goodness is something that involves all men, and the ethical basis of behaviour varies greatly according to religion and race, caste and class, even by age and sex. Throughout the history of Western civilization, men have thought about ethical behaviour only in terms of relationships between human beings. Each in its own way every community has acted on Protagoras' dictum that man is the measure of all things. In the East, philosophers have, in principle at least, applied ethical rules to man's behaviour toward other living species as well as his own, and in the last one hundred years a certain sense of responsibility towards some of the higher animals has developed in the West. But nowhere has this side of ethics anything like the significance of its humanly oriented aspects. These in themselves are complex and controversial enough. There is, however, one universally acceptable contention, that vigorous health appropriate to an individual's age is good and desirable. I may be prejudiced by my training in medicine, but I believe that any observant adult can recognize at once a really healthy individual, man, woman or child, and that this can be confirmed objectively by a physician. It is unequivocally better to be healthy than to be ill or disabled. In the modern world, to be healthy has some important social implications. It means family and school education in healthy living; it means child-health centres, immunization against infectious disease, school dental services. There must be good water-supply and sanitation, and if health once lost is to be regained, there must be good hospitals and good doctors. In the last analysis, all these things take for granted a high standard of living throughout the community, which in its turn demands a developed technologically based civilization and an interest by governments in the health of all their citizens.

No people or government would deny that it is good:

1 to ensure for every individual the fullest measure of health that is allowed by his inheritance.

The healthy individual must have mental as well as physical health and, perhaps, the main requirement for mental health is that the mind should have the opportunity to function to full capacity. The intelligent socially-adaptable congenially-occupied individual can be recognized as easily in Russia or China as in Australia or Japan. Everywhere he is recognized as desirable, and the ostensible objective of education is to produce such people.

It is in relation to education that one sees most clearly the intensely human characteristic of genetically determined influences which make it more easy to learn or to excel in one field rather than another. No one can become an artist or a mathematician without appropriate education, but there are multitudes of intelligent children who, with the best education in the world, would never be more than mediocre as either. When an adolescent finds his or her real bent at school or university and can follow it, his joy in learning is as evident to others as to himself. Ideally, the aim should be to devise a system which, within a general education, can provide ways by which the full potential of intellectual and manipulative skills of each individual can be recognized and fostered.

There is much more to a man than the skills he can learn. The visceral emotional aspects of thought and behaviour are equally subject to an infinite range of genetic variability. No matter what form of measure is applied, whether it is one of the conventional IQ tests, any examination or other test of achievement or any measurement of temperament, every group of children will show something like the standard bell-shaped curve in the distribution of qualities. Just as for height or weight, or any other character determined by the interaction of many genetic factors, there will be many around the average and progressively fewer as we approach the two extremes, very tall or very short, very bright or very dull.

In matters such as temperament and aggressiveness, individuals at the two extremes may be too far from the norm for them to take any place in a free society. They have to be classed as insane and no one has found an answer to that problem. But for the great majority of sane individuals, with their range of intelligence and aptitude from genius to mediocrity and dullness, and from the born musician or mathematician to the inept, an ideal education should be such as to allow each individual to realize his own particular talents to the benefit of the community and of himself.

One could condense that into the second rule of a biologist's ethic, which is:

2 to provide for every individual the education which will allow him to develop his intellectual and manipulative capacities to the full.

Bodily health and a well-trained mind are good in themselves, but there is a third aspect of life which I believe is equally acceptable to all people as good. This is that achievement and success should be recognized. It is part of the wisdom of the ages that within every human organization there must be hierarchies of prestige. The desire for status, in the extreme for fame, 'that last infirmity of noble mind', is a deep-seated biological quality of the mind. Fortunately, there are so many thousands of different fields within which a man or woman may excel that it is a rare individual who will not, at one time or another, feel that he leads the way in his chosen pursuit. It is, too, one of the pleasanter aspects of our species that people tend to feel pleasure in seeing another person gain success or prestige in any of all those activities in which they themselves are not competitors.

The third rule of our biological ethic then becomes:

3 to ensure to all the opportunity for achievement and the recognition of success.

There is probably no government on earth which does not pay at least lip-service to each of those rules. In the Scandinavian countries, practice corresponds very closely to the ideal and, in all, there is a general acceptance of the importance of health, education and achievement. It is obvious that, even in Scandinavia, an intelligent attempt by the community to provide these basic human needs to every citizen does not bring happiness to all. All that we can reasonably claim is that this represents a necessary attitude for all governments to adopt in relation to the people for whom they are responsible. One might even take the point of view that these are almost the only legitimate ways in which government should interfere *positively* in its relation to the citizen. Maintenance of 'law and order' by restriction of one sort or another would be necessary even in a community of saints, but that can be left for discussion in Chapter Eight.

So far, I have been concerned only with the rights of the individual as they are seen by a medical biologist. But the individual is part of the species, and the biologist's chief consideration must be the indefinite continuation of the species or its continuing evolution along lines which can be regarded as consistent with the criteria that we now consider important. I believe that it is inadmissible to lay down any programme for change at the evolutionary level. No competent biologist now takes seriously the claims that man can look forward to guiding his own evolution. There is, however, a much more limited but, I believe, a legitimate objective to be stated as the fourth of our rules:

4   to ensure that opportunity to attain bodily and mental health and to find satisfaction in achievement will be available to all future generations in measure not inferior to what we now enjoy.

Implicit in that rule are the actions needed to bring the under-privileged communities up to the level of health and comfort enjoyed by affluent countries around 1955–60. Equally implicit, and perhaps even more difficult to implement, are the actions needed by and within the affluent and militarily powerful countries. Somehow, the exponential impossibilities described in Chapter Two must be checked and reversed before it is too late. World population must be stabilized. The world's stock-pile of bombs must be defused and got rid of. My ultimate dream of human sanity is that one of my grand-children should watch the world's last intrusion into outer space when the last giant rocket sends the last of the nuclear war-heads to orbit eternally and harmlessly round the sun! The other ethical requirements concern less directly human matters, they cover the broad need for conservation, for the retention of those features of our planet which we should wish our descendants to enjoy. Put categorically they are as follows:

1   The non-recurrent resources of the planet, high-grade mineral ores, fossil fuels, shall be used with discretion until it is certain that acceptable substitutes from recurrent resources will be always available.

2   The recurrent resources, that is, those based essentially on the inflow of solar energy, shall be maintained so that they can be used indefinitely at an optimal level. This applies specially to food and other products obtained from plants and animals.

3   Human action must not be allowed to induce large-scale alteration in the world's climate.

4   Life is something which evolved specifically in the earth's surface environment. The biosphere must not be poisoned by the accumulation of non-biological materials, including sources of excessive radiation.

5   It is essential for aesthetic and cultural reasons—and in the last analysis, these are biological reasons—that large areas of country shall be retained as national parks, wilderness reserves, and the like, to allow the preservation of all significant forms of wild life and of many areas of natural beauty or of geological or historical significance.

Again, most modern governments pay lip-service to these aspirations and probably no academics will seriously question their desirability. But where action for long-term conservation clashes with immediate profit, there is never any doubt about the alternative to be chosen. One of the worst examples in Australia has been the senseless haste to exhaust what are clearly limited sources of oil and natural gas at a time when the same material can be imported more cheaply from the Middle East. Clearly, the same insane destruction of our rarer mineral resources is already being enthusiastically undertaken. The men concerned know what they are doing and offer their justifications. Reserves are

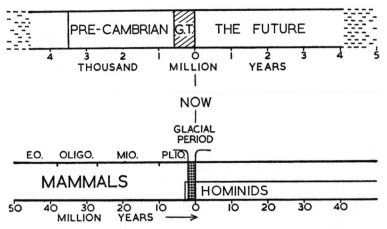

Fig. 6 The background of time. The upper figure shows the period of 8–10 thousand million years allotted to the earth's existence as a solid body and as an abode of life. The shaded area (G.T.) covers the time from the early Cambrian, usually taken as the beginning of geological time. The lower figure shows the Age of Mammals from the Eocene onward, with the Pleistocene glacial period shaded, and the time over which man, his immediate ancestors and his descendants (Hominids) have existed and may be expected to exist.

assessed and some reasonable guesses made on the size of 'probable' reserves. Making due allowance for technical progress in such matters as the localization of ore bodies deep below the surface and the economic use of low-grade ores, there is a consensus of opinion that at least the next hundred years can be provided for. No one feels that it is necessary to take thought for more than that hundred years. We are interested in the year 2000, but no one thinks forward to 3000—and it appears that the essential features of the earth as a home for living things will persist for a few *thousand million* years.

Sir Charles Darwin, who was a famous physicist as well as the grandson of the greatest of all biologists, wrote a book which he called *The Next Million Years*, in which he attempted to forecast the large-scale pattern of future human history. He chose one million years as a round figure because it represents the approximate time it takes a species of large mammal to evolve into a new species. A million years ago, our ancestral population presumably had characteristics intermediate between *Australopithecus* and *Homo erectus*. All members of that population would be clearly differentiable from any form of present-day *Homo sapiens*. Almost anything can happen in a million years—two more ice ages, for instance—and it is quite impossible to forecast how much change in human structure and biochemical function will have taken place. There may be very little, or *Homo* may have given rise to several distinct species. If one is to choose a time over which to think of man's future, I believe that a million years is more appropriate than a hundred years or than 4-5,000,000,000 years.

The thesis I want to develop grows naturally out of the presentation of a biologist's ethics. It is that the earth is the only conceivable home for the human species and that, unless by his own action or by some cosmic catastrophe, man is wholly exterminated, he and his descendant species will remain the dominant organism on the planet for its whole duration. To me, this presents the imperative that through all the geological periods in front of us the ideal must be preserved that, within the limits of climate and physical structure of the earth, it must be maintained as a basically stable human ecosystem.

Ecology is the study of the overall interactions of an organism with its environment, including particularly the other living organisms in that environment. Everyone is aware of the broad requirements of air, food and water for any mammal including man; only a professional ecologist will realize the intense complexity of the conditions which allow a living species, anything from a virus to man, to survive and prosper. On the surface of the land, for a foot or two into the soil, and through sea and fresh water there is what we call the biosphere, an immensely complex web of life, of interacting organisms and the non-living materials that pass in and out of living material. For some purposes, we have to consider the biosphere as a whole. If we are interested, for example, in the oxygen-carbon dioxide cycle, we have to balance the fixation of carbon by green plants on land or in the upper layers of the sea against the liberation of fixed carbon by the respiration of animals, or by the burning of wood produced in the last century, or of coal which represents carbon drawn from atmospheric carbon dioxide some 250 million years ago.

For most purposes, we take a more limited field for study and speak of such units as ecosystems. To take one example which can point a moral, we might consider the surface water of the southern oceans that ring Antarctica. This is where commercial whaling is destroying the last of the great whalebone whales and with them the industry itself. The whales have evolved a completely specialized type of feeding by filtering out of great volumes of surface water small crustaceans, 'krill', which are present in such numbers as to allow a young whale to grow at the rate of one to two tons per month. The krill feed on smaller organisms, which in their turn feed on microscopic green algae. The primary needs of the algae are sunshine, carbon dioxide, the upwelling of water relatively rich in phosphate and nitrate, and traces of other elements present in sea water. This particular 'food chain' is inter-meshed with many others to make up the ecosystem as a whole. The algae and other micro-organisms of the surface layers provide food for a wide variety of small animal forms, many embryonic, some mature, which collectively form the plankton. Dozens of species of small fish live on plankton and themselves form the prey of larger fish. Penguins eat fish, leopard-seals eat penguins, killer-whales eat seals and dolphins and can kill the giant whales, leaving the carcasses to end up as food for hundreds of species of sea scavengers. Over the millennia before whalers entered the south seas, all these organisms existed in a fluctuating equilibrium that, by and large, kept the numbers of each species roughly constant. The whalebone whales were the largest and longest-lived components of the ecosystem and, until large-scale factory ship whaling in the twentieth century, one could say that the southern oceans provided a stable ecosystem for these whales. As in so many other ecosystems, the fatal impact of man and his commercial rapacity has changed all that.

There are hundreds of other types of ecosystem, a coral reef, a mangrove swamp, an Australian fern gully, an African savannah, and so on. Two hundred years ago, one could have discussed the Australian Aborigines in Victoria as part of a stabilized ecosystem in the eucalypt forests and grasslands, with kangaroos and emus the more conspicuous of a wide range of marsupials and birds. Only when man is a nomadic food-gatherer can he be regarded as part of a primitive ecosystem. Once he became a settled farmer with crops and domestic animals, man had to dominate the shape of any ecosystem of which he formed a part. As soon as permanent settlements were established anywhere, the population had to make a living, to utilize the environment to provide food and shelter. In one way or another, a more or less stable human ecosystem came into being. The history of agriculture is largely the story of how ways were found, by rotation of crops, by the use of animal manure and, eventually, of superphosphate and more sophisticated fertilizers, to retain the fertility of soil from one generation to the next. In essence, each agricultural community should, on the average, begin each Spring with land as good as it was the previous year. That is the criterion of a stable human ecosystem.

In a world where Australian wheat goes to China and the phosphate to grow it comes from Nauru, where iron ore goes from Australia to Japan and returns in part as heavy mining equipment to produce more iron ore, it is obvious that any meaningful human ecosystem must cover the world. If we are to have a stable human ecosystem for the earth, then at the beginning of each decade we should have a world in as good a shape as it was ten years before. Since the earth is a closed system receiving nothing of significance from outside except solar energy then, sooner or later, we must find ways of using solar energy to replace what has been used up. Only then will it be legitimate to think of the world as a stable human ecosystem.

In the process of reaching the primary requirement of a stable human population level, it is clearly inescapable that a level far above the optimal one must be tolerated, perhaps for centuries. This is almost certain to destroy all the natural ecosystems in those parts of the earth suitable for food production. In the process, many forms of wild life and many plant species will vanish. This will have to be accepted, but in addition there are bound to be difficulties in moving from a natural ecosystem—a normal ecological climax is the technical term—to a managed ecosystem designed for maximal human benefit. In the intensely cultivated areas of Europe and North America, most of the local difficulties have been understood and overcome, but with each new area to be brought into production there will be new problems to be dealt with.

The primary requirement for a stable human ecosystem is stabilization of human numbers. This is something much more than the conventional aim of family-planning, which is that every family should have the children they want, when they want them. It means that at some point it becomes obligatory that each generation replaces itself and no more, that the average number of live births per woman during her lifetime shall be two plus a fraction (probably between 0.3 and 0.9) to allow for couples who are non-fertile, and for childhood deaths. In a modern, affluent society in which death from child-birth is extremely rare and of which the possibility virtually never enters into a woman's thoughts, the minimum demand of any healthy and happily-married woman is 'one of each'. To obtain a baby of each sex, simple statistical rules show that a relatively large number of families, 25 per cent, would need to have four or more children to be sure of one of each. If every family stopped when, and only when that aim was achieved, the mean family size would be three. In the same areas of affluent society it is rather common to be told that the ideal family is four. Advanced countries like America and Australia will probably find it almost as difficult to bring birth-rates down to what is required, as India or South America.

There must have been deliberate interference with normal reproductive processes to check undue population growth since the dawn of history. Infanticide was legitimate or obligatory in many primitive societies, as well as in classical Greece and Rome, for a variety of reasons. Many primitive peoples have a folklore on semi-poisonous plants with supposed contraceptive powers and crude forms of mechanical contraception have been used for centuries. Dangerous but effective methods of inducing abortion by insertion of a freshly peeled withy or similar object into the uterus are probably equally ancient. Only in recent years, however, has there been deliberate scientific and socially accepted research to devise better or more acceptable contraceptive methods and simultaneously find ways of persuading women to use them effectively. I can see no point in discussing technical aspects of contraception or elaborating on social and psychological factors in the family-planning approach. It is the necessary first step to population control. What I am interested in are the types of social actions which may need to be tried before population control becomes possible. Some assumptions will be necessary for any such discussion, so, for fairly obvious reasons, it is convenient to choose a country with a broad resemblance to Australia. We assume (a) that it is a democratically ruled nation-state; (b) that it is not under external duress; and (c) has voluntarily agreed to maintain a population of, say, twenty-five millions. We assume also that the possibility of war, or of any other cause of disastrous depopulation, epidemics, cosmic catastrophes, etc., is left out of consideration.

In a democratic country there can be no overt discrimination on the basis of wealth, education or colour. If population control has been adopted, every couple will have the right to two children, with the State's blessing. The only restriction against childbearing that could be acceptable would be a known probability of 25 per cent, or greater, that a medically significant and socially disabling congenital defect will be present in the child. The most straightforward approach would be to provide substantial child endowment for all couples other than any in this small group, but only for the first two children. The striking fall in the birthrate during the great Depression of 1930–34 indicates that monetary factors could be very potent in determining fertility. A third or fourth child would not be eligible for child endowment, but that is probably as far as one need go. There is no justification for elaborating the detail of what is still an unthinkable situation for most people. Somehow it will be necessary to provide ways by which childless couples can adopt children, but how it will be done can wait on the future.

In parenthesis, it should be pointed out that if one's ideal for the world is a gradual enlargement of the gene pool in every country till, in effect, all racial differences are soft-edged, adoption of infants offers by far the best approach. If third or fourth Australian babies were adopted by childless couples in India, China and Japan, and vice versa, all gene pools would be enlarged and strengthened without the troubles which are inevitable when cultural differences must enter the country, along with the desired genetic qualities, in the course of adult immigration. Public education would be needed to make such a policy acceptable, but, again, monetary incentives could be helpful.

As far as one can gather from the current situation, the problem will always be to lower rather than to raise the birth-rate. This would justify implementing the widely growing opinion that any woman who is pregnant less than one hundred days should be entitled to an abortion on request. In whatever way population control would be implemented, social and personal problems would be frequent and difficult. It would be axiomatic that Australia, like every other nation-state, would have a permanent demographic commission to advise government on any trends away from what is desired and the means within what was politically or socially possible by which they should be countered.

Every responsible citizen of the over-crowded developing countries, of which India and Pakistan are representative, is aware of the menace of uncontrolled population growth. Most such countries are attempting positive action, but the difficulties of introducing Western-type family-planning, let alone effective population control, are almost insuperable.

In the first place, there is the ignorance, lack of motivation and often simple mental incapacity to be found in many women, particularly, but not exclusively, in primitive communities. In

Haiti, more than half those lost to the study series organized by Pincus just did not or could not follow the instructions on how to take oral contraceptives.

To establish family-planning as a first step toward population control will always be expensive. Oral contraception costs around two dollars a month in Australia, which is beyond the means of a poor and primitive population. Correct insertion of IUD's (intra-uterine devices), plus control and replacement where necessary, requires skilled advice. It has been said that at least one doctor per 3–4,000 population is needed to cover population control work alone. In fact, the ratio of all doctors to population in the world as a whole is far smaller than this. Figures for around 1963 were: one doctor to less than a thousand population in the USSR, USA, Australia and Western Europe, while in India the figure was 1:6,200, and in Africa, excluding South Africa and the UAR, 1:20,000. Nurses and the other para-medical personnel are in similar short supply in every country in which the need of birth-control guidance is specially urgent. The widespread use of birth control clearly will not come until a rising standard of living allows the support of an adequate pro-portion of medically trained personnel and auxiliary services. It is significant that the only Asian country that has significantly curbed its rate of population increase, Japan, has more than one doctor per 1,000 of the population. Only with such an adequate supply of trained personnel could abortion be safely used as a deliberate procedure for population control.

In thinking about the provision of medical care in relation to population control, there are two other important aspects to be considered. The first concerns the medical benefits of fertility control to mother and children, quite apart from its social sig-nificance. Pregnancy has many lethal and non-lethal compli-cations in primitive society, vesico-vaginal fistula being one of the commonest and most distressing. Diseases like tuberculosis tend to be accentuated during pregnancy or in the post-partum period. Even in a prosperous society there are significant com-plications and dangers of pregnancy. There are occasional undesirable side-effects from the regular use of contraceptive pills, but these are statistically far less than the complications that would be associated with the pregnancies they prevent. At quite a different but equally important level, if maternal affection and physical care is essential for the mental, social and physical development to normality in children, a small family is better than a large one.

The second aspect may be even more important. In any society living on the edge of hunger it is essential that old people should be supported by their children if they are to survive at all. The extended family with three generations living in the same house or equivalent social unit is, or was almost universal in most communities. Even in Western countries it has faded away only within the last one hundred years. In India, and most Asian countries, it still persists. In the absence of old-age pensions and the welfare state, the only way to make provision for one's old age in an undeveloped community is to have enough children to ensure that two or three of them will survive to full maturity. In the old days, to do that could require eight to fourteen pregnancies. For any type of population control to be effective there must be clear, easily-understood reasons that a simple woman can grasp why it is better that she should have two children rather than ten. It is not likely that she would be convinced unless she was persuaded that both of those two children would outlive her and her husband and provide comfort for their old age.

This may be the most important of all reasons for pressing ahead with preventive medicine in every region of the world. The basic requirements can be anything from medical schools and research institutes to drainage of malarial country, or helicopter ambulances. In practice, it is a matter of improving the national income as rapidly as possible and so disposing of what money and man-power is available that the requirements for health and for population control are met with approximately equal effectiveness, while general education, agriculture and industrial development keep in step with them both.

Effective population control is not only a medical and an economic problem. It is, at a very deep level, going to be determined by human motivations and the impact of cultural pressures on these. These pressures can be both religious and political, both acting characteristically to oppose birth control.

There are special difficulties in introducing population control in predominantly Catholic under-developed countries. Some remarks made by the late Gregory Pincus in 1967 are worth quoting:

'I would say that the Catholic Church is the biggest impediment that I know of to the spread of adequate means of birth control and its use throughout the world. Fortunately, it is not a very great impediment. In Puerto Rico . . . religious objections to the use of oral contraceptives accounted for the refusal of only about one one woman in a hundred.'

A less easily recognized political difficulty was mentioned by Dr Candau, Director of the World Health Organization, who, in the same discussion, said:

'The great obstacles to birth control in many countries are: (i) the existence of minority groups anxious to increase their numbers and their political influence. This, with all the implications involved, deters a government [from action] though, for obvious reasons, it is not publicized; (ii) the desire of white populations not to give the impression that they are afraid of being numerically overwhelmed by populations of other colours.'

European races have been increasing rapidly since about 1750, the coloured races started at least a hundred years later. As another demographer said:

'it is therefore highly provocative if the white races . . . approach in a tactless way the question of increase of the coloured races . . . in Africa these feelings are very strong . . . I know of only one African country where the government has overcome this point and specifically asked for assistance in population control.'

Discussion of the genetic dangers of radioactive fall-out has allowed most people to understand the use of the term 'genetic burden' as a measure of the number of potentially harmful genes that a person carries. As I have discussed already (p. 112), most harmful genes are rare and recessive, that is, they will not produce manifestly harmful results unless two such genes are contributed, one from each parent. In a family where this can happen, one in four of the children will, on the average, be a 'double recessive' and show the harmful trait. A potentially harmful recessive gene arises by spontaneous mutation. This is always a rare occurrence, but it can be calculated that the well-known 'sex-linked' mutation responsible for haemophilia (or 'bleeding') happens at a rate of about 1:100,000 per generation. This means that in every 100,000 births there will be one child with a newly formed mutant gene for haemophilia. The disease is often fatal in males and most geneticists accept that, unless the current developments in the treatment of haemophilia are changing the situation, there is a virtual balance in which a genetic death occurs for each new mutation. A genetic death means simply that a carrier of a harmful gene dies without passing the gene to any descendants.

If persons carrying harmful genes are enabled by medical or social developments to be responsible for a larger proportion of the next generation of children, the balance will be lost and the harmful gene could be expected to spread like a slow infectious disease. Muller once calculated that if people with haemophilia could be kept healthy enough to have as many children as unaffected people, then in 50,000 generations half the human race would suffer from haemophilia. Very similar reasoning could be applied to other dominant or sex-linked genetic abnormalities of medical significance. There has been talk of eugenic mating as a means of improving the quality of human beings since the days of Galton, and somewhat more realistic claims for the necessity of some action to prevent significant increase in the burden of harmful genes. There are still some who believe that future advances in the understanding of genetics will, in principle, allow deliberate genetic control that could make the future evolution of the species man's own responsibility. Just as domestic animals can be bred to almost any type that is desired by generations of breeders, so, it has been suggested, men could be made to evolve toward a more desirable type, or at least a healthier one.

The current temper of genetics is almost wholly against any attempt to dabble in eugenics at population level. Genetic disabilities are numerous and important, but any attempt to handle them must be at the level of the individual and his family. The standard present-day approach when an infant is born with genetic disability indicative of a 'double recessive' is to attempt to ameliorate the condition by whatever means are to hand. To take three of the common conditions, cystic fibrosis will require special treatment of all infections, an albino's life must be so arranged to shelter skin and eyes against sunlight, while, with a phenylketonuric child, efforts will be made to provide him with a diet containing the smallest practicable amount of phenylalanine. In none of these conditions can the sufferer lead a normal life. In all of them it is unlikely that an affected person will marry. As soon as such a condition is recognized in a child, one can be certain that both parents are carriers. There will therefore always be a 1:4 likelihood that any further children will be abnormal, and most geneticists would counsel against having more children and offer early abortion should pregnancy occur.

The fact that abortion will eliminate three healthy foetuses for each abnormal one would be a significant disadvantage if there were any serious dearth of births in the community at the time. It is probably quite unacceptable now—maybe it will always be unacceptable—but, from the point of view of everyone concerned, the logical thing would be to extend the current practice of obstetricians in not allowing grossly deformed infants to live. No doctor would dream of trying to help an anencephalic monster (born with no brain) or an incomplete conjoint ('Siamese') twin to survive. In my view, it is equally illogical to spend months or years keeping a genetically abnormal infant alive in hospital through some elaborate method of counter-acting a biochemical defect, or to condemn another to life in an institution for the feeble-minded. In a sane society, we can expect a progressive approach toward the screening of new-born infants for all the important biochemical and chromosomal defects. Those for whom there is no promise of a tolerable life will, after independent confirmation of the diagnosis, be eliminated as circumspectly as is now done for a gross anatomical abnormality. As at present, any form of killing, whether of a deformed infant or of a patient in the final stages of cancer, is legally murder; a long process of public education will be necessary before any such policy will be adopted. Euthanasia for the elderly sufferer has been widely discussed, but the greater need to spare the congenitally incurable from the long misery of life is still not a subject for public discussion. It should be made clear that 'mercy killing' of genetically abnormal infants would have virtually no effect as a eugenic measure. It could only be advocated on humanitarian grounds.

Should it become general throughout the world that the vast majority of couples limit themselves to two children and that virtually all children survive to reproductive age, there would eventually be genetic difficulties. Evolution up to man has depended on a rather brutal winnowing for survival of the large excess of young produced. It is wholly unbiological for a mammal to produce only two young during a pair's reproductive life. What would happen in a thousand generations is hard to visualize. Perhaps the most likely result is a random accumulation of minor inefficiencies not too dissimilar to the process of ageing in the individual. Something of the sort may already be happening in relation to minor eye defects, allergies and migraine. It is impossible at present to see any practicable way out of such an impasse, if it develops. Two possibilities may be worth thinking about. The first is to expand the variety of human genes available by increasingly wide cross-racial matings. The second is to carry out very extensive and long-continued studies on the medical aspects of human inheritance, including the relatively minor disabilities I have mentioned. With modern large-scale data-processing facilities the whole population of a relatively stable small country like Denmark, or a largish island like Okinawa or Tasmania, could, in principle, be followed for a hundred years to cover three or four generations. This could be one of the large-scale high-level research projects dealing with contemporary change which I spoke of earlier (p. 93) as being needed to replace laboratory research when the Age of Discovery has ended.

It is conceivable that, on the basis of such long-term studies, it might be possible to initiate a programme to minimize genetic deterioration. Perhaps it would take the form of supplying incentives, appropriate to some far-distant era, by which couples, according to their genetic potentialities, would be persuaded to have the 0, 1, 2, 3 or 4 children that the State or its experts considered would do most to maintain genetic quality. Something else that may need to be kept in mind is that the last human group to emerge from the primitive high birth-rate-high death-rate condition may also maintain its genetic integrity more effectively than the people who accepted civilization too soon.

eight

CONFLICT, CRIME AND WAR

In the discussion of dominance in Chapter Three, I stressed the similarity of the peck-order in chickens and other hierarchies of dominance in animals to the hierarchical structure of most human groups. There is, however, an additional uniquely human phenomenon which intrudes into virtually any conflict situation, whether between individuals or between rival groups of men. This is the imputation of guilt, in one form or the other, to one's antagonist. Basically, guilt arises when an individual in some form of conflict situation acts in a fashion which does not conform to what is socially acceptable. By convention, guilt calls for punishment. Whether the twin concepts of guilt and punishment arise automatically from the process of learning in infancy and childhood, or have some more complex origin, they are deeply implanted in most human beings. A sense of guilt is one of the commonest symptoms in mental disorders and one that can readily be induced in many people, well within the limits of normality. This is a standard part of the technique of religious conversion or of political confession in totalitarian regimes. The socially harmful effects of this human obsession with guilt and punishment can be seen in many, perhaps most, aspects of conflict in modern life.

To an extra-terrestrial intelligence, the statistics of road accidents involving human injury and loss of life would probably represent an interesting exercise in probability theory. There is almost the same regularity in the numbers killed per annum in relation to density of cars per road-mile, standard cruising-speed, age and sex of drivers as we find in the gas laws where volume, pressure and temperature are all related to individually random molecular velocities and collisions. Yet every road accident is investigated from the point of view of who was to blame for its occurrence. Once that has been determined, the guilty person, which has come in practice to mean his insurance company, is liable to pay for the damage to the other car and the hospital expenses and loss of future earning capacity of those injured.

Anyone who has ever driven a car can recall occasions when he has known that he has made an error of judgement which could have rendered him liable to massive payments, if for some otherwise wholly fortuitous reason a collision *had* occurred at that time. It is obvious to every newspaper reader that if an accident involves as the (possibly) guilty person the driver of a vehicle owned by a government, or any wealthy organization, there is highly likely to be an action for damages by anyone who suffers chronic disability as a result of the accident. No such remedy is available unless someone or some corporation can be found guilty. If a driver is rendered paraplegic for life by an equally random occurrence, a skid at speed which crashes the car into a tree for example, he gets no compensation.

In quite a different field we have a worker's compensation for injury associated with his employment. It is well known to every dermatologist that skin disease attributed, often correctly, to exposure to some industrial chemical will never clear up with any treatment so long as a compensation claim is unsettled. The same holds equally for a 'strained back'. Until justice is felt to be done by the receipt of compensation, the injury fails to heal. It is an interesting contrast that quite severe strains and bruises received on the football-field are almost all completely recovered from and the player in the team again within a few weeks. Clearly, from the point of view of the happy functioning of society the second situation, where there is a positive incentive to get well, is infinitely preferable.

The obsession with the allocation of blame, of finding who was guilty whenever something undesirable happens, runs right through the workings of current society. In a divorce, there is in most countries a guilty partner and there are money penalties against him. There is, fortunately, a growing realization that the only sane ground for divorce is the irretrievable break-down of the marriage. Once that has happened, divorce should be automatic and the necessary financial adjustments made between the parties must take into account the well-being of all the parties concerned, the children most of all. The question of guilt on one or the other side is immaterial, unless the actions involved indicate a need for psychiatric investigation and treatment.

Where we fall down worst of all is in regard to the punishment for crime. Whenever there is a police strike, or some other break-down in social structure, looting and violence always break out; whenever goods are in transit, pilfering occurs. There are more drug addicts amongst doctors and nurses than in any other social group; every year one or two solicitors are convicted of wrongfully using a client's funds. Dozens of cars are stolen every day in every city in the Western world. There can be no question that a majority of people will undertake an anti-social action if it offers them benefit and, in their opinion, there is no chance of their being found out. A smaller, but still substantial proportion will balance the benefit against the risk involved and, according to temperament, take the gamble when the odds seem to be in their favour. No community has ever been able to function without some mechanism for protecting itself against anti-social action, against crime.

The standard deterrent is punishment of crime by imprisonment, that is, segregation of the individual from normal social contacts, including sexual ones, allowing him, however, relatively free contact with other criminals and in an environment where sadistic and homosexual practices are almost impossible to avoid. The only thing that can be said in favour of imprisonment is that it keeps a proportion of dangerous (psychopathic) criminals where they can harm only other members of the prison population.

The concept of personal responsibility for anti-social action is deeply ingrained in all human societies, so is the tradition of punishment by imprisonment. Change is, however, under way.

Hanging, or its equivalent, was the standard punishment for murder or rape seventy years ago and only two hundred years ago for many forms of theft. Capital punishment has gone from most Western countries and further modifications in the handling of crime and criminals are inevitable. To many people, and perhaps especially to biologists, the whole pattern of guilt and punishment is an archaic one. They would say that conviction for crime calls not for retribution but for action which will be therapeutic and deterrent, to convert the wrong-doer, if it is at all possible, to one who has a fair chance of becoming and persisting as a law-abiding citizen.

I believe that this is a theme worth developing, and at the risk of sounding naïve and platitudinous I should like to start by saying something about the process of learning. A biologist is liable to be accused, especially by educationalists and psychologists, of putting too much weight on genetic characteristics and tending to forget how much more significant is cultural inheritance passed on by imitation, authority and the spoken or written word. This suspicion is justified only in the sense that every biologist must remain convinced that the interaction of genetic factors with past experience and the immediate environment is concerned in every human action. Behaviour of any sort is dependent on the anatomical structure of the nervous system and its functional integrity. I have already used Washburn's phrase about the genetic basis of behaviour as being based on neural configurations which make some types of behaviour much *easier to learn* than others. Every human biologist is as convinced as anyone else that social attitudes, as well as specific information of all sorts, is passed on by imitation, learning or authority from one generation to the next.

In line with the general approach of this book, the nature of learning needs first to be looked at as it can be seen at work in the mammals and birds that are available for scientific study. Rhesus monkeys, rats and pigeons have been the chief laboratory subjects, though once, for an hour or so, I assisted at experiments on teaching octopuses to learn the difference between a square and a rectangle at the Zoological Station in Naples! The details of behaviour as they are determined by the immediate situation have to be learned, however deeply based genetically the general character and aim of the behaviour may be. It will be learnt in part from the parents, in part by the actual experience of the young animal. Out of the studies of learning by rats and pigeons has come the general concept that learning by animals (and children) is speeded up, and indeed probably determined by what is called positive or negative reinforcement. In more every-day terms, this means that to induce learning, one must provide appropriate rewards and punishment. The experimental psychologist who was working with octopuses at Naples rewarded the octopus with a piece of fish if it made the right response, and gave a mild electric shock when the animal made a mistake. With rats or pigeons the reward is a food pellet, but in all such experiments the procedure is essentially similar. One important point is that positive or negative reinforcement must be given soon after the response if the necessary nerve pathways to make the right response habitual are to be laid down. Put into common-sense but not necessarily accurate terms, the animal must know to what action the reward or punishment applies. Common sense and immemorial usage indicate the same processes apply to human beings.

Most anthropologists and social scientists would agree that, within the limits of genetically determined aspects of brain function, the capacity of a child to grow up so that he fits easily into a human community—and this includes those qualities we ascribe to conscience, decency, moral sense, conformity to law and custom—is acquired from other human beings. The process closely resembles what can be observed in the laboratory. Good behaviour, that is, behaviour which is admired or tolerated by the dominant members of the community, is not inculcated by any intellectual or logical process. In the formation of socially acceptable behaviour, reward may be replaced by praise or by heightened expression of affection, and physical punishment by reprimand or 'withdrawal of affection'. These still, however, are forms of positive and negative reinforcement and, as such, unrelated to strictly logical action.

Behaviour can often be quite irrational. We touch wood when we make what suddenly seems a rashly optimistic statement, street numbers tend to go directly from 12 to 14, and when we visit an Eastern holy-place we take off our shoes with the rest. In discussing such superstitions a year or two ago, I mentioned an interesting experimental approach to superstitions, the word being used in simple objective sense of those attitudes and habits which have no visible social usefulness to an outside observer. It came from a popularized account by Arthur Koestler of an experiment made in the course of Skinner's research on learning in pigeons:

'Instead of setting one of his experimental cages in the usual fashion, so that when the pigeon did some specific act like pecking at a button or turning its head to the right it received a pellet of food or a dozen grains of wheat as a reward, he presented the bird with a random situation. The machine was set to give the reward at irregular intervals with no regard to the bird's behaviour. After this had been going on for two days, an extraordinary situation developed in which almost every bird had adopted some unusual posture or activity depending apparently on what it happened to be doing immediately before random largesse appeared. If, on two occasions or more, there was positive reinforcement of a certain action and the bird kept on repeating the action, it would inevitably be reinforced further. But every bird had, by simple accident of circumstance, adopted a different wholly illogical, unbiological action as appropriate to be rewarded by the random appearance of food. In many ways, this can be taken as a model for the inculcation of superstition, if we define superstition as meaningless actions which are "believed" to promise rewards or allow punishments to be avoided.'

This approach may throw some light on the development in adolescents of delinquency and criminality. If a boy experiences a sequence of positive reinforcements from his first pre-criminal actions, whether petty theft, sexual misdemeanour or violence, the pattern of behaviour will become more and more firmly established. This seems normal enough. Looking simply at man as a mammal, acquisition of desired objects, normal sexual activity and successful conflict with another are all gratifying activities of patterns that have been deeply engraved during primate and human evolution. The civilizing process is basically to find means of restraining these activities within limits that allow a tolerable community life. Restraint is much easier for some people than for others.

There is an infinite variety of temperament and personality among men, but many psychologists believe that two main types can be more or less clearly recognized. Perhaps more correctly, we can see a range of temperaments in which the two extremes can be clearly differentiated as what Eysenck calls introvert and extrovert types. In most respects, these are nearly synonymous with Sheldon's cerebrotonic and somatonic types of temperament. In trying to define an introvert, a medical bias is useful. I have always remembered an early twentieth-century physician's description of the type of man who in middle life suffered from duodenal ulcer: quiet, not very sociable, with an obsessional demand for perfection in his work, likely to marry the first woman who takes an interest in him and not to stray from her—the sort of man who is responsible for much of the higher-level work that keeps the community on a reasonably even keel—the introvert type. Eysenck adds some other qualities: a high degree of suggestibility, with the related capacities of loyalty and at least overt conformity to the pattern of his society. He is, at all times, law-abiding, but can suffer greatly when two of his legitimate loyalties conflict. I think that almost every sentence I have written in this book marks me as a rather extreme example of the introvert type.

The extrovert type is for me completely characterized in two lines from Kipling:

> Four things greater than all things are—
> Women and Horses and Power and War.

It is of the nature of the introvert to admire the extrovert and probably the main reason why, in my adolescence, Kipling was my favourite reading was that my attitude was very much that of Beetle to Stalky. Like Kipling himself, my admiration and loyalty would go to the extrovert rather than to an introvert—always provided he had quality. Temperament is not directly correlated with ability. Most 'colourful' people are extroverts, so are most criminals, and so also, of course, are most of those who have been able to rise through politics to high public office.

In this chapter, I am specially concerned with the difficulties that may well make quite impossible the changes which well-meaning introverts, who dream of a peaceful or even tolerable world, call for in their writings. More important than anything else is the complexity and variety of the intellectual, emotional and temperamental endowments amongst individuals. Any attempt to generalize about human behaviour must bear this variety very much in mind. The differences run deep. The introvert, for example, finds it relatively easy to abandon cigarettes as soon as he is convinced of their danger to health, the extrovert's good resolutions break down repeatedly. The academic scholar or scientist is most frequently, but by no means invariably, an introvert. The man keen on the conservation of wild life or sensitive to the danger of environmental pollution will usually be an introvert; wild-game hunters, duck-shooters, explorers and pioneers are predominantly extroverts. One might almost say that the extrovert is the man with the courage and the force to act according to his nature, and for that very reason he is the more likely to disturb or disrupt a functioning community.

Extrovert and introvert are applicable to persons well within the limits of normal sane human beings. But human variety goes far beyond what can be regarded as normal. Men can be highly intelligent, yet suffer from manic-depressive insanity, which is in some way a far-out extreme of the extrovert temperament, from schizophrenia, which has a similar relation to introversion, or from paranoia, which allows him to suffer from highly systematized delusions in one field—usually delusions of persecution—while sane in regard to all matters which do not impinge upon the area of his delusions. When we look more widely over the field of mental disease, we can find every combination of brain damage with mental abnormalities. Amongst important types of structural damage or anomaly in the nervous system there are several forms of genetic abnormality, traumatic damage by bullet or severe concussion, infection by bacteria or viruses and a variety of degenerations in middle and late life. All of these will show some deficiency of mental function and on top of a general deficiency there will often be evidence of one of the psychoses I have mentioned earlier.

It is the law that if a man is manifestly insane he is not to be held responsible for acts which in a more normal individual would be criminal. The psychotic is a patient to be treated by a psychiatrist, not to be imprisoned or punished in some other way. Modern treatment makes much use of drugs which can modify mood or temperament and are often of particular value in, as it were, damping down symptoms sufficiently to bring the patient back into normal social life. For more deep-seated mental disease, 'shock' treatment is widely used and is often effective for a time at least. The most potent and controllable of such treatments is ECT (electro-convulsive therapy) in which the patient is rendered briefly unconscious, in something resembling an epileptic fit, by the passage of a controlled electric current through his brain.

No one questions the propriety of such treatment of individuals suffering from psychoses and there have been many suggestions that there is an equal justification for exploring the treatment of other types of anti-social behaviour by such methods rather than by imprisonment. Eysenck has suggested that we know enough about the effect of some drugs on the introvert-extrovert balance of temperament to open up interesting possibilities. Alcohol tends to weaken the inhibitions and fears of the introvert and is liable to make the behaviour of the extrovert even more socially intolerable. Amphetamine and similar drugs act in the opposite direction and could conceivably be used in potentially delinquent extroverts, on the assumption that social rehabilitation could be rendered more effective by intelligent use of such drugs.

There is a strong public and judicial prejudice against any use of drugs, or of what can be called 'brain-washing', to change a man's relationship to his community against his wish. But this brings us into some important and highly debatable territory. Most religions have used techniques of 'conversion' to bring outsiders of any type into conformity with an 'in' religious group and have often tortured and killed those who resisted the process. In modern techniques of hot- and cold-war, ideological indoctrination is an essential weapon and may be referred to as political indoctrination, brain-washing, de-Nazification, or rehabilitation, according to place and circumstance. Psychiatrists have become deeply interested in these techniques and analogous aspects of other cultures. Sargent has written much on these comparative aspects. In his view there is much in common between:

(a) religious conversion in unsophisticated communities;
(b) the techniques of African witch-doctors for casting out devils, who have possessed, by hypothesis, people with various mental disturbances;
(c) brain-washing as a cold-war weapon; and
(d) the ECT or insulin-shock treatment of the psychiatrist.

In all of these the manipulator's aim is to use psychological means, drugs, physical agents, or some combination to produce a complete break-down of control of behaviour. This leaves a fertile soil, as it were, for the implantation of new attitudes to society and new behaviour patterns.

In Western countries this type of action is acceptable (1) in psychiatric clinics, (2) in revivalist religious meetings, and (3) in training servicemen to resist brain-washing techniques. It is anathema to all minority political groups and there is a deep-seated and well-based distrust amongst the great majority of citizens against any deliberate use of such methods to change human attitudes or behaviour, except within the three acceptable categories. There is also a strong emotional distaste for any significant measures being taken against criminals and delinquents beyond segregation from the community. This holds even more strongly for actions of highly anti-social character which do not fall into conventional categories of crime, such as large-scale financial frauds or the exertion of aggressive ambition in ways that damage the general well-being.

There are, however, quiet moves being made to reform penology—most modern prisons have a resident or consultant psychiatrist and one can reasonably expect a slow movement toward treating and rehabilitating the criminal rather than punishing him. One interesting feature of convulsive therapy is that the experience is a highly unpleasant one and, as such, could have a deterrent as well as therapeutic effect. A combination of ECT followed by group rehabilitation sessions and parole after a few weeks' treatment could be a much more hopeful method of reclaiming criminals in the making than any current methods of punishment.

There is an interesting support for this approach in a recent book by Menninger who refers to the changes in the style of punishment for social misdemeanours since the days of the Puritans. In the Massachusetts Bay Colony, thieves and liars were set in the stocks, blasphemers were stood in the pillory and whipped. Punishment was painful, carried out in public and derogatory to the individual, but it was short. Indefinite segregation from the community, whether to mines or workhouses or to prisons, was something alien to the Puritan sense that all men were sinners. Only when authority saw the wrong-doer as someone wholly different from and inferior to himself did imprisonment become the standard punishment.

It is not too far from the Calvinist doctrine of original sin to the modern liberal opinion that we are as prone to social sickness as to physical disease, and that to deal effectively with both we have no need to be constrained within concepts of guilt and retribution.

Crime and war must be equated. Basically, we have all been aware of this, but only in recent years has it become allowable to speak openly about it. The change is due to the increased public consciousness of the intermediate forms of conflict and violence. Conscription for military service in Western countries excuses from service both those who can demonstrate genuine conscientious objection to war and those who are physically, mentally and morally unfit. The last category includes confirmed criminals. Such an attitude was reasonable in days when war was a straight-forward conflict between two relatively homogeneous nation-states. Things are no longer so simple—probably they never were.

Within any large country there are criminal sub-cultures, sometimes with a very hard core indeed, but always soft-edged with a wide fringe of the unfortunate, the grasping and the psychopathic. This is an even bigger essentially normal group who can be drawn by circumstance into criminal association. In one sense, the whole of life in a large human community is a struggle to reach a progressively higher place in some hierarchy of power, and for the great majority the only clear index of power is money. We all want more money and we go about getting it in our own variety of ways.

Every group of wage- and salary-earners has its own way of exerting pressure for progressive increases. The strike technique has crept up into the white-collar jobs and has been very effectively applied by jet airline pilots. Other highly paid professions have less overt but effective methods of keeping up with any general increase in prosperity, and, when opportunity offers, obtaining special privilege for a particular group. At the individual level, there is a wide range of ways by which additional money can be obtained: by extra work, by luck in lotteries or on the horses, or by all the sub-criminal and criminal ways that can bring ill-gotten gains.

The criminal sub-culture is composed of those ready to use all expedient opportunities to gain power, that is, money, with minimal regard to the conventional rights of others. In a real sense, they are at war with society. Quite frequently in the history of American crime one considerable group of criminals has been at war with another and there is always cheating, blackmail, informing and murder associated with conflict within the sub-culture. At times the resemblance to guerilla warfare is very close. It becomes even closer when minority groups with acute economic grievances initiate violence. This invariably brings criminals and psychopaths to seek advantage out of the conflict.

Armed revolution and guerilla-type civil war is only a step away from this if the aggrieved group is large enough and it is possible for them to obtain arms. In the first stages, the illegal provision of arms by gun-running, or otherwise, will be assigned to criminal or sub-criminal elements. Spies and agents provocateur acting on behalf of any outside supporters will necessarily comprise a majority of criminals.

From there to a Vietnam-type war is an almost insignificant step. It may be reasonable for an American President to feel that American intervention in Vietnam was a justifiable police measure, but it has been rendered completely ineffective because another major power does not accept the right of Americans to police the situation to their own advantage. The USSR has, therefore, supplied adequate munitions to allow successful frustration of all American efforts to control or pacify South Vietnam. It has had to be accepted by the Americans that the Russians can send unlimited ships carrying munitions to Haiphong without hindrance. An effective blockade would end the war, but it cannot be considered on account of the threat of Russian nuclear power. The crux of the present position is that the United States and the USSR cannot make war directly on each other. They can only interfere in a conflict nominally involving others. The reason, of course, is that all-out war now involves national suicide.

It is obvious to everyone, even the generals and missile masters, that the advance of science and technology has made war by advanced nations biologically absurd. Since the end of the Second World War the United States has spent some $2,000,000,000,000, two thousand billion dollars, on defence. In 1969, it is in the process of vastly increasing the rate of spending by the construction of an ABM (anti-ballistic missile) system and by the development of MIRV (multiple independently-targeted re-entry vehicles), a system of offensive weapons designed to overcome any type of enemy ABM system. The Russians are active along the same lines, with an additional interest of their own in developing weapon-carrying satellites. It has been clear for at least six years that the existing situation is such that a nuclear war between the USA and the USSR would be completely destructive to both countries and quite possibly exterminate most life on the planet.

To quote a recent article by H. F. York, the current position in America is a manifestation of the danger mentioned by Eisenhower when he left the White House, 'the danger that public policy could itself become the captive of a scientific-technological élite'. York's conclusion is that the process called by the professionals in think-tanks on strategy 'worst-case analysis' and used by both sides leads to an impossibility of ever-reaching parity in mutual deterrence and eliminates most conceivable approaches to progressive disarmament. What he says of the United States is equally applicable to the USSR. 'There is no technical solution to the dilemma of the steady *decrease* in our national security that, for more than twenty years, has accompanied the steady increase of our military power.'

If there had been no megaton bombs, there would have been equally lethal developments of chemical and bacteriological warfare, both of which could, in principle, be raised to the same genocidal level as we have with the nuclear weapons.

Clearly, security and disarmament are political and biological problems—which are being rendered insoluble by the scientific-technological and industrial complexes on both sides acting under their own insane logic of progress.

The mutual posture of the two super powers has made it inevitable that intrigue and undeclared wars in which opposing sides are supported by the two major antagonists should exist in many parts of the world, particularly in South-East Asia. The undeclared wars are fought with 'conventional' weapons and everywhere in the world politicians, if they are not in a position to make or buy nuclear weapons, are building up their old-fashioned armies, navies and air forces.

Even in Australia our politicians talk as if war—1939-45-type war—was the most natural thing in the world and that we must waste a billion dollars a year in preparing for it.

There are two approaches to the prevention of war that are talked about. Simultaneous and complete disarmament, ostensibly supported by Russia, phased reduction of armaments with mutual inspection, which is the nominal policy of America and the West. Nothing whatever has been achieved or seems likely to be achieved.

A cynical realist might well feel that the only possibility of a peaceful world is its emergence from the chaos of a nuclear war in which one ruling group would be left with sufficient power and the will to use it to disarm the rest of the world. This is a cold-blooded horror that must somehow be avoided. The only 'scientific' approach to the problem of war and peace derives from statistical study of men killed in 'deadly quarrels', to use L. F. Richardson's phrase in the first of such studies, and of defence expenditure of major countries over the years. Results give some depressing confirmations of the obvious, but little more. The other approach to peace research is by the use of the mathematical logic of game-theory on very highly simplified models. It seems self-evident that such models can be no more than interesting intellectual exercises. In the real world, as K. E. Boulding points out in a recent review of the topic, any political situation is dominated by a small number of decision-makers, is muddied by secrecy and deception, and can perhaps be summed up by saying that where a choice must be made between two possible results, A and B, the chance of giving the answer which will subsequently be validated by the event is 50 per cent!

For a long time, and probably indefinitely, international politics will never be subject to accurate prediction. New ideas may come from intuition or analogy, and will only be tested if they can seep through to the notice of a sufficiency of people at decision-making level and influence them in a fashion closer to common sense than to game-theory. Even if there seems to be no other realistic way of achieving that stable human ecosystem that we must all dream of than through nuclear destruction, that might well end the human race for ever, there is an indirect approach. Can we conceive of a system of peace-keeping which, *if it could once be established*, would without requiring any major alteration in human nature have a reasonable likelihood of being effective? In asking that question I am very much aware of its Utopian character, just as I have to accept Popper's dictum that Utopianism is dangerous, pernicious and self-defeating. I should much prefer some type of piecemeal social engineering which searches for and fights against the most urgent evils of society, rather than, in Popper's words, to choose an ideal state of society as the aim which all our political actions should serve. The justification for asking the question is that the greatest and most urgent evils, nationalism and nuclear armaments, are not susceptible to piecemeal action.

The history of the United Nations leaves one wholly pessimistic about the possibility of a gradual increase in its authority and effectiveness. No one with any understanding of human affairs can imagine a unitary governing body for the world as we know it. With the neutralization of the USA and Russia by their lethal antagonism, any hope of modifying crude nationalism by the application of simple ecological principles and common sense has been lost. Black Africa presents an object lesson with its extraordinary proliferation of non-viable nation-states. In virtually every instance, the nation has come from the upgrading of administrative areas the boundaries of which had been drawn in the nineteenth century by the colonial powers. It is depressing to find that not one of the successor States of the African colonies has allowed any minority areas within its borders to be transferred to an adjacent State to which the minority was tribally related. There has been no attempt to improve the position by using ecological and ethnic criteria as a basis for political units. As cynics have remarked for many years, the only real criterion of 'independence' by which a nation gains the right to a seat in the UN General Assembly is its possession of armed forces under its own control. Every new nation has sought the appropriate weapons and has found them in profusion supplied by developed countries in one or both of the major power groups. In most of the under-developed countries there is either a frank military dictatorship or a one-party régime with army support. The holders of power will only relinquish it to superior violence.

Nationalism has become too potent a force or too popular a catch-cry and the USA–USSR antagonism too crippling to allow an effective police-force to be developed within the UN. Any solution to the problem of maintaining world peace must be one which can still allow the continuation of sovereign nation-states capable of defending themselves against physical aggression and of maintaining order, according to their own understanding of order, within their boundaries.

There has been a general contention amongst those interested in world peace that an effective UN police-force is incompatible with national sovereignty over internal affairs. With a little imagination, however, it is possible to picture a situation which (a) would allow a nation to retain armed forces with which it could effectively resist any invasion of its territory either by an aggressor nation or by a 'world police'-force, yet at the same time (b) provide an effective international organization which could maintain peace without being capable of interfering directly with a nation's internal activities.

The simplest approach to such a situation comes from a suggestion, which has been raised by both Russian and American scientists, that the wealth of the seas should provide, through royalties or otherwise, a source of funds for UN activities which would not be dependent on contributions from its Member States. In November 1969, Canada raised the matter in the UN Political Committee of the General Assembly by suggesting that the UN reserve up to 80 per cent of the bottom of every sea and ocean 'for the benefit of mankind'. This has the implication that if a world organization administers wealth-producing facilities beneath the seas, it must have some way of protecting and policing them. This provides a central requirement around which to envisage the political and military conditions needed.

What follows is a bald and brief attempt to state in outline what those conditions might be:

1 The existent boundaries of nation-states, as defined by military control, are not subject to change, except by mutual consent of the two States concerned.

2 Within each State, law, order and population control is to be the responsibility of its government, chosen and changed according to political forces within the country, without interference from any world organization. Any type of army or police may be maintained, but no armed sea-going ships or aircraft, except for small patrol-boats and helicopters needed for police action.

3 The world organization (WO) alone will possess armed ships and aircraft in number sufficient to impose an effective blockade on any aggressor and to carry out all necessary police duties in regard to commercial sea and air activities.

4 The chief safeguard against the WO forces interfering in the internal affairs of any State will be that its air- and naval-bases shall be on small islands, artificial if necessary, strategically disposed around the globe.

5 All personnel of the WO forces retain their nationality and domicile and, except for a core of career excutives, all personnel have a limited term of service. The ruling board or cabinet members to be limited to a five-year non-renewable appointment.

6 Funds for the support of WO forces will be in the form of royalties from wealth drawn from the sea beyond the three-mile, or some other agreed limit of national sovereignty.

This approach, in a certain sense, looks to re-introduce the situation that existed from about 1865 to 1910 when the combination of British naval power, using for the most part overseas bases which were not permanent domiciles of British citizens—Gibraltar, Malta, Aden, Trincomalee, Singapore, Hong Kong, Walfisch Bay—with the Monroe Doctrine of the United States, allowed uninterrupted freedom of commerce on the seas and progressive political development in most parts of the world.

The limitation of national sovereignty to the land occupied by the nation is based on the human instinct or instinctively based tradition that the individual, and any larger group with which he identifies himself, has a defined and personal relationship to certain areas of land and that trespass by individual or alien group on that land is resented and must be resisted. As my medical-assistant friend from the Solomon Islands told me (p. 79), primitive people have no similar instinctive reactions toward the sea or the air. Claims to sovereignty there are all based on the military or commercial calculations of power-seeking individuals or groups. Of course, every vested interest which has been established in sea or air will resist loss of their control of a profitable resource. They will endeavour to present the position so that it provokes the same emotional response as invasion of the land. But in a modern world, disillusioned about the infallibility of those with political and commercial power, this may not be an insuperable obstacle.

The virtues of such an arrangement can be looked at first from the point of view of the world police-force. As the guardian of widely spread under-sea facilities it must obviously use armed ships and aircraft. Its island bases will provide both immunity from attack and automatically limit the police-force activities to its proper functions. The only land under police-force control, the island bases, supports no population from which an army of occupation to take over a recalcitrant State could be drawn. Equally, if a major State made any attempt to take over a police base, it would have to attack it—according to hypothesis—with troops carried on civil-type ships and aircraft. Adequate protection of the base by warships and fighter aircraft would make any such attempt a disastrous failure.

From the Member Nations' point of view, each will still be able to take any local defensive measures that conservatism and mistrust of neighbours or the police-force seem to call for. Each nation will have the right to exclude any individuals who are not nationals of the country and use any necessary force to do so. The only types of national misdemeanour calling for police action would be the crossing of a frontier by force and perhaps government-sponsored smuggling of arms into another country. Air- and sea-blockade is the only punitive measure that the police-force can apply.

It would be an easy enough exercise to elaborate a Wellsian Utopia on that basis, but there would be no justification whatever for doing so. All that I have in mind is to throw out a suggestion which I believe is a new one, as to how a stable global ecosystem could be policed in its earliest stages. As I have tried to suggest, it is not wholly unrelated to past and present political aspirations. It is, however, quite another matter to attempt to outline the political actions which could lead to the transformation. There is no easy road between what exists in 1969–70, and what I have suggested could be a self-perpetuating basis for the minimum of central control needed to maintain a peaceful world. What is needed first is that sufficient people should feel the need for a stable human ecosystem and accept the necessity of having a sufficiency of power in the hands of a world authority to rule out any possibility of the overthrow of the peacefully evolving ecosystem by violence. Once it was widely enough appreciated that world peace, with security and without any abrogation of national sovereignty, was a practical possibility, political pressures would soon force those in national authority to find steps within the art of the possible to bring the solution into existence. There is already the beginning of an international Civil Service and there are many points at which a start could be made at building up the facilities and personnel for a WO force. Even now, sympathetic governments could initiate feasibility studies on the potential, as bases, of islands under their jurisdiction. More immediately useful could be a concerted effort by internationally minded scientists to persuade governments to accept the principle that any wealth from the oceans shall be under international control, and make the definition of ocean as close to the shoreline as is politically feasible.

There is, I believe, an interesting analogy to what has been suggested at the international (or supranational) level to be seen in the evolution of the monarchy in such countries as England and Japan. To a logical individual, the 'right' of a nation to provide vast homicidal apparatus that could quite conceivably exterminate the whole human species is at least as absurd as the Divine Right of Kings ever was. But the king as the apex of a hierarchy of status and prestige had and has a valuable social function which never had any necessary relationship to claims of infallibility and absolute power. A constitutional monarchy persists in the three Scandinavian countries which lead the world in real democracy and in the two most politically stable 'great powers', the United Kingdom and Japan. It could well happen that some or all these monarchies will pass quietly away in the next few decades, but for an interim period they have had a stabilizing and useful political role. In a rather similar fashion, the nation-state has good justification for its existence based on reasons other than its possession of arms and the power to use them in war.

If to preserve those useful functions it is necessary to use the traditional decorations of army and artillery, that is a small price to pay—something exactly equivalent to the pomp and ceremony of a British royal occasion.

nine

THE
OBSTACLES
IN THE WAY

If I can judge from what is being said and written by men and women with scientific training who are interested in social problems, most such people would agree that the concept of a stable human ecosystem for the earth (SHEFTE) is a legitimate aspiration. Perhaps I can emphasize the importance of the concept by a superficial reference to a mathematical field the theme of which has the rather piquant title of 'random walk'. It has some important applications to topics, like Brownian movement of minute particles in fluid and genetic change in an animal population, but for our purpose one can take it literally. Let us suppose we have a blind man who, in addition, has lost any sense of the direction in which he is moving his legs. He goes on walking, but where he puts his next step is wholly random.

To make it easier to illustrate the process, in Figure 7 (*opposite*) we are only considering movement to left or right. We forget about forwards and backwards, and instead put a time dimension into the figure. Since we are dealing with a mathematical abstraction, we can make any rules we like. Our blind man is random walking on an indefinitely long area bounded on one side by a precipice and on the other by a flexible conveyor-belt a few feet below the edge, which will carry anyone who falls on to it to some abode of bliss. If the walker moves at random, he can go on moving until one of two things happens—either he falls over the right-hand precipice and is killed, or he falls on to the conveyor-belt and is whisked off to the happy land. Both are final states —with them the random walk is over. Perhaps a glance at the figure will show how, applying the concept to human history,

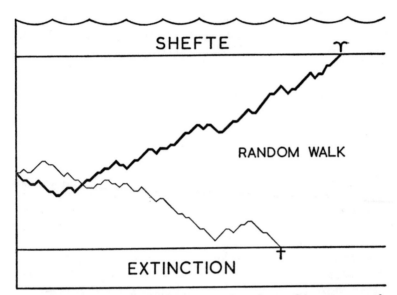

Fig. 7 A diagram to suggest the concept of 'random walk' going on until one or other of two stable situations ends the walk. For the human species, the alternatives are extinction or a stable human ecosystem for the earth (SHEFTE).

there are only two possible final states—extinction of the species and SHEFTE—but there is no way of saying when the final state must be reached. It may well be that, several times, we must come close to extinction before the stable continuing situation at last emerges. From our own point of view in 1969–70, it is no answer to our dilemma to suggest that in forty years' time there will be a complete destruction of civilization but still a sufficient residue of genetically sound enough human beings to ensure that in a thousand years another civilization will make a second try to produce a viable world ecosystem. For myself, I want to spare my grand-children from chaos and to hope that they will live to see *their* grand-children getting ready to bring that stable ecosystem into being.

Nevertheless, it is only a tiny minority who think that way. To speak of SHEFTE makes no sense to us, and even less to the great majority of men, if there is no way of reaching it except through an agonizing 'random walk' through centuries or millennia of human misery. We have to ask: What are the obstacles and how are they to be overcome? It is the modern version of the *Pilgrim's Progress*: what are the 'forces of evil' that prevent Everyman from reaching the Celestial City?

It is not very difficult to define 'evil' in our present context. It is any action by a man, or by groups of men, aimed at obtaining power (or its equivalent in money and the like) by methods unacceptable to those currently in power in the community being considered. In any large modern country there are many thousands of communities demarcated in geographical, occupational, religious, and other ways. An individual will almost always be simultaneously a member of several different communities, but in any of them he will almost automatically resent and brand as evil any breaking of the rules which govern status in that community. Breaches may take a thousand different forms, from the attack on Pearl Harbour or a military coup, to theft of unpublished scientific information or cheating at cards. It is axiomatic that the dominant members of any hierarchy will indignantly and, if necessary, violently oppose any efforts by others either to replace them in their positions of power by unorthodox means or to eliminate the power structure itself.

In Australia, taken just as an example of the Western world, we have two immense hierarchical obstructions to the primary requirements of SHEFTE, which are population control and elimination of the possibility of war. The first is the Roman Catholic Church, which has thoroughly grasped the Darwinian principle that the only biological measure of fitness is the number of offspring who survive to reproductive age. No outsider could possibly understand the theological arguments against birth control, but it is perfectly obvious that the political reasons are cogent. If the rest of a country practises birth control, and good Catholics have six to eight children all duly indoctrinated in their turn, then the country soon has a majority of Catholics. It is immaterial that most Catholics behave normally and have reasonably-sized families, but there can hardly fail to be a net gain in succeeding generations for any group which uses opposition to birth control as a means of increasing its power in the community. There can be no question but that any move which appeared to be making serious progress toward SHEFTE would be fought tooth and nail by the Church.

There are equally formidable obstructions to effective advance in the limitation of war. The whole picture is, of course, overshadowed by the nuclear balance of terror between America and Russia. From the military angle, Australia is completely insignificant. Yet, as Australians we must be interested, and it is fairly easy to assess the general attitude of people in responsible positions in the armed services, politics or business. Ideas in regard to Australian military security are based on the traditions of British military and naval history and of Australian experience in the First and Second World Wars, plus the present sense of dependence on the United States for protection against a vaguely visualized communist threat from Asia.

The great majority of those responsible for Australian policy accept the conventional postures of the nation-state as a personified image and as such take the realist point of view that we must be ready to defend ourselves, but, in addition, make sure that we have 'great and powerful friends' who we hope will support us in future difficulties. No one seems to have realized more than superficially that the bombs have totally changed the character of war. The close-fought Australian election in October 1969 threw interesting light on the almost universal attitude of Australians. All three major parties underlined that they were deeply concerned in defending Australia against any aggressor at something around a billion dollars per annum. The average man knows that to gain or to keep anything he desires, he has to be aggressive about it. The nation very roughly approximates to an image of himself as he imagines he would feel and act in the absence of both a system of law and a policeman. It will be a long time before the average moderately law-abiding citizen will want to undestand, let alone support the SHEFTE idea.

In an early chapter I drew the moral from peck-order amongst chickens that altruism is only possible where dominance is undisputed. Man is a much more complex organism than a chicken, much more varied and labile in his behaviour than any other mammal, but that aphorism interpreted with appropriate subtlety still holds. Those who endowed the great charitable foundations, Nobel, Rockefeller, Ford, Nuffield, Gulbenkian, were, no doubt, moved by complex motives, but each was, financially speaking, above the battle. At the other end of the scale, the saints and the martyrs, from St Francis of Assisi downward, have, for the most, been sure of their personal communion with God, and when a man knows that he is in the very confidence of the Almighty he is dominant indeed. No doubt there are exceptions in cultures other than our own, Gandhi perhaps the greatest. But, for people of European descent, my experience and my reading reiterate that altruism in any more than a trivial sense is possible only where dominance is complete.

I believe that the principle can be legitimately applied to what may be the most hopeful aspect of the present day—the interest of scientists in public affairs. As I have said earlier, a scientist, if he has any professional competence, will occasionally make a discovery or enunciate an idea which for a month or two, or even a few years, will put him at the top of a little hierarchy that means a great deal to him. He is the world's top expert in one corner of his chosen field and for a little he can feel the glory, and the goodwill toward all, of greatness.

On an August day in 1897, Ronald Ross saw and understood the significance of malarial oöcysts in the stomach wall of a mosquito which, two days previously, had been allowed to feed on a patient in an acute attack of malaria. Two days later he sent his wife a poem:

> This day relenting God
> Hath placed within my hand
> A wondrous thing . . .
> With tears and toiling Breath
> I find thy cunning seeds
> O million murdering Death.
> I know this little thing
> A myriad men will save.

Poor clumsy verse, maybe, but I think it makes my point.

Ross, with those who went before and who came after him, in due course made the elimination of malaria possible and, more than any other single factor, sparked off the population explosion of the tropical lands. The graph of Mauritius that I placed on page 26 tells the story more clearly than any words. It is only proper that, two full generations after Ross, the chemists working on reproductive hormones should produce that combination of two hormone-related substances which is The Pill, and which in time may bring back the ecological balance that was thrown off calamitously by too great a good.

I can agree with a statement—an overstatement perhaps—in a recent paper by Dennis Gabor: 'Power addicts must be excluded from power', in other words, the meek must inherit the earth; but how do we get there? *We* are the only hope, and in saying 'we', I class myself with the always enlarging group of men and women who have used their status in science to preach the gospel of responsibility to the 'power addicts' who continue to rule the world. Amongst physical scientists, Einstein, Oppenheimer, Szilard, Rotblat, Gabor and Pauling come to mind, and perhaps as the first I should have placed Alfred Nobel. The biologists are not so well known to the general reader, but Julian Huxley, J. B. S. Haldane, J. M. Needham, Barry Commoner, Bentley Glass, and René Dubos can be taken as representative of the two main English-speaking countries. There are hundreds more, and in the last year there has even emerged the voice of a famous Russian physicist, Sakharov, speaking in the same tone. The Pugwash meetings have already had some effect in helping on the slow process of mutual understanding of the problems of disarmament. There is probably more active concern over wild-life conservation and the limitation of environmental pollution now than at any previous time. U Thant has recently called a conference on environmental deterioration for 1972. After discussing the changes in progress, he said that 'no nation can any longer be isolated from these global pressures. It has become clear that we live in one biosphere within which space and resources, though vast, are limited.' This comes close to asking for action for a stable human ecosystem which will necessarily involve the whole biosphere.

The pervading pressure of the ideas of human ecology is beginning to work. I like to remember the great Victorian reformers, Bentham, Wilberforce, Chadwick and Farr, Darwin and Huxley, and Florence Nightingale. Each in their own way developed and disseminated ideas which, without violence and without any real influence on or action by the masses of the people, gradually became part of the accepted ideas of educated people. A man of a later generation who exerted a similar effect on the thought of economists and statesmen was J. M. Keynes, who himself said: 'The power of vested interests is vastly exaggerated compared with the gradual encroachment of ideas.' There can be no doubt that the idea of a global human ecosystem is moving in men's minds. It may be impossible to see a direct approach, but if the idea becomes widely enough established it must exert a bias on all actions which seem likely either to help or to hinder in bringing the idea to fruition.

Environmental damage, pollution, the need for conservation of wild life—it is a group of problems relatively easy to discuss. There will be no wholly discordant voices at the United Nations conference and obstruction to the implementation of what may be asked for will be hidden rather than open. It is significant that there has also been no overt opposition to the activities of the World Health Organization, until it became involved very late and very ineffectively in birth-control programmes. But U Thant knows, and Dr Candau (Director-General of WHO) knows that conservation of the world's resources and control of world health are futile in the long-run unless population is stabilized and brought down to a tolerable level and until the likelihood of major war is reduced to vanishing point. Not so many would agree with me that there is a final requirement almost equally essential, that 'technological progress and national growth' be slowed down and the effort be turned instead to the civilization of the under-developed countries of the world.

I have already quoted President Eisenhower's warning as he retired from the White House, of 'the danger that public policy could itself become the captive of a scientific-technological élite'. I used the quotation in discussing how impossible it has proved to prevent a progressive increase in the power complexity and expensiveness of armaments without, at the same time, gaining any improved security against retaliatory action. This, too, is what Eisenhower was concerned with, but the same phenomenon of irresponsible and irresistible pressure for technological innovation can be seen in many other fields, some in science and some in industry. Something is clearly technically possible. It will be new and it may well bring profit: therefore there must be action and once action has begun, a new vested interest is created. Few actions fail to do harm to someone, and technological innovations almost regularly lead to long-term difficulties that may be hard to overcome. Until the full implications are seen in the real world it may be very hard to decide whether the overall effect of the innovation is on the right or the wrong side of the balance.

One of the most obvious examples is in space exploration. The motivation for Kennedy's call for a man to be put on the moon and brought back to earth before 1970 was, in part, a matter of national prestige, in part a quest for possible new weapons' systems. Scientific objectives have been emphasized, but, so far, have been of secondary importance. In the process of achieving the objective, America has built up an enormous scientific and technological organization for which new tasks must be found. There is, undoubtedly, much more of scientific interest to be obtained from lunar exploration, but it is most unlikely to include any information relevant to human benefit. Conceivably, effective occupation of the moon could confer some military advantage on the occupying power. A major observatory on the moon, if it could be built and maintained, would undoubtedly provide fantastically interesting new material for astronomers. There may be 100,000 astronomers and people with informed interest in astronomy in the world, but for the other 99.997 per cent of the population, nothing won from the lunar observatory would have any influence whatever.

What will be attempted next is still under discussion. There is strong pressure on the US Government to proclaim that a manned landing and exploration of Mars will be made in the early 1980s. This should be technically feasible by then and should cost no more than the approximate $5,000 million per annum that has been used for the moon project. This is additional to continued lunar exploration and unmanned planetary probes. The primary objective of the Martian venture is to obtain samples of any life on the planet. Secondary ones are to obtain scientific information bearing on the structure of the planets and the history of the solar system.

A visit to Mars could have no military significance. The pictures that have already been obtained suggest that Mars is as sterile as the moon. Any Martian life can hardly be more than some lowly micro-organism that may have found it possible to exist and proliferate in an extraordinarily inhospitable environment, perhaps as a terminal relict of a brief period billions of years ago when early stages of evolution might have been accomplished. If such micro-organisms are brought back to Earth, there are two extreme possibilities. (1) They may be dangerously pathogenic for anything from a single terrestrial species to the whole of the biosphere. (2) They may be cultivable only under conditions reproducing their Martian environment and have no direct bearing for good or ill on human affairs. I should guess that the second is at least a million times more likely than the first alternative.

I am enough of an experimental biologist to have an unholy interest in the biochemical processes which might have been evolved as the basis of life on Mars. For what may be as many as a million people who are interested superficially or deeply in the interaction of nucleic acid and protein or the early stages of evolution at the chemical level, the results obtained would be fascinating. But again their only human implication would be as a potential danger. I know my own kind well enough to be certain that studies would be made on the interaction of Martian with terrestrial genetic materials. Nothing might come of it, but if anything did, the possibility of a dangerously different pathogen arising would again have to be considered.

No one can give reasons for thinking that anything brought back from Mars can be of the slightest human benefit. Just conceivably, it might do unimaginable harm. Like Pascal's wager, there is only one way to win. Yet one can feel absolutely certain that NASA will go on with plans for bringing material from Mars to the earth.

On earlier pages I have already mentioned other examples. The development of factory-ships and chasers with harpoon guns was a logical application of technology to whaling which will undoubtedly destroy the industry and, in all probability, exterminate all the commercially interesting species. Modern drugs can be very potent, often life-saving when properly used, but there are few which are not positively dangerous to some people under some circumstances. It is another example of technological momentum to find that amongst the several hundred cases of fatal bone-marrow paralysis, due to the often-valuable drug chloramphenicol, that have been investigated, only in 6 per cent of the cases was the drug called for in terms of good medical practice. No less than 12 per cent of the fatal cases received the drug as treatment for a common cold or mild respiratory infection.

The supersonic aircraft—Concorde or Boeing SST—that no one wanted, have also been discussed. Yet technological momentum will undoubtedly force them upon the world.

If controlled hydrogen fusion reactions can ever be used to produce nuclear power, the reactors will be made irrespective of the dangers of malfunction and liberation of toxic isotopes.

A new example could probably be added to such a list every few months and it is probably only my ignorance of much of modern technology that has left my own list so short. This chapter is, however, concerned with more than enumerating the obstacles in the way of the achievement of a viable global ecosystem. It must also discuss whether there are possibilities of overcoming the obstacles.

In a real sense, the intrinsic momentum of science and technology is responsible for most of the hopes and all the major dangers of the modern world. Only science has been powerful enough to upset all the norms of animal ecology as they had

developed. Only science has the potentiality of righting what
has gone wrong. Science and technology, being the work of men,
are only reflections of human motivation. Technological momentum, as I have discussed already, results primarily from the desire
for recognition of achievement. Just as in the learning process in
animals, reward is only effective when it is given immediately
after the animal carries out the 'right' action, so prestige in science
or technology, as in the arts, is appreciated and effective only
on the short term. The man whose discovery comes too soon for
its significance to be recognized by his contemporaries gains
neither prestige nor profit. Babbage invented the computer, but
he had been dead for seventy years before what he had tried to
do with cog-wheels and a steam engine became electronically a
practical possibility. His life was that of a frustrated, bad-
tempered, misunderstood and unhappy man. The modern tech-
nologist wants to see results and profit within a year or two, not
to have the long-term results assessed for fifty years before his
credit for the innovation is adequately recognized and rewarded.
It is obviously no easy matter to find how to counter what springs
from a very deep-seated human quality.

No reasonable solution seems possible in a society where
prestige and profit are the principal driving forces, unless some
arbitrary change in the circumstances which bring prestige and
profit can be engineered. Even then, a large number of people
with plenty of influence must first want to bring about such a
change. Any attempt to hold back this almost irresistible
momentum of technological innovation would have to use a
highly sophisticated combination of economic and legislative
actions, any one of which seems frankly inconceivable under
present Western conditions. The first, and perhaps the only one
that could be politically possible would be for government to
insist on a thorough and time-consuming analysis by public
authority of the potential social impact of any significant technological innovation—something analogous to what the Food
and Drugs Administration (FDA) of the United States is now
demanding of new drugs. The second would be to manipulate
downwards the present financial rewards for innovation, for

example, by making technical information open to all, without patents or royalty and by sharply diminishing plant depreciation allowances.

The third would be the most difficult of all, to attract away from industry to academic research, or other pursuits, most of the men capable of real technological innovation. It may underline the difficulty when I confess that when I think about what would be to Australia's immediate benefit, I can strongly support the opposite view. Things being as they are, and as a matter of piecemeal social engineering, it would help Australian prosperity if universities paid more attention to training scientists for industry than to conditioning all their best graduates to aim at a career of pure research in the universities or the CSIRO. In Britain, the Minister of Technology and the President of the Royal Society think the same. But when I try to take the wider view in terms of the affluent world as a whole, then I believe that, in one way or another, we must include action of this sort if we are to slacken the technological momentum. Probably it will never be done deliberately, but we can never be sure that unformulated processes moving in that direction are not already at work.

There are probably only two real possibilities of countering destructive potentialities of technology. (1) If the population expansion could be slowed down and reversed, a major incentive to economic growth would be removed. It is only when a market is expanding steadily that it is financially easy to incur the expense of thorough-going innovation in methods of manufacture. (2) If we can eventually overcome the complex social difficulties that hold back the economic take-off in most of the developing countries, there may be a period when the manufacturing capacity of the affluent countries can be largely diverted to the needs of the poorer two-thirds of the world. There is a desperate need for capacity to make things and, for what could well be an important interim period for redeployment of resources, much of the Western manufacturing capacity could be turned to designing, making and setting up the sort of factories that the countries of Africa, Southern Asia and South America need. These are not

1975 models, automated monsters run by a few highly-skilled technicians, but 1930–55 models that will still require a relatively large work-force but will produce very large amounts of the things most needed, especially what is required to raise the productivity of the land. A whole-hearted move of this sort might make it possible to slow down production for home use and so to limit waste, pollution and environmental destruction in the advanced countries.

I am perfectly aware that such an approach will be anathema to every profit-making business-man and to every orthodox economist. Their criterion of progress, of goodness, for any country is the size of the annual percentage advance in the GNP, corrected for the real value of money and for population change. This is the natural attitude, firmly based on male aggressiveness and female pleasure in conspicuous consumption, and manifested in the hierarchical structure of any industrial society, capitalist or communist.

The dilemma must be squarely faced. Somehow, and in a time less than a hundred years, action to convert this planet into a stable human ecosystem must be firmly under way. Unless this happens, the exponential impossibilities will bring chaos and possible extermination of most life on earth. Yet every instinctive drive of human beings bred into them in a million years of evolution is opposed to the actions needed to build that global ecosystem. The difficulties may be insurmountable, but if they are to be overcome it can only be by the application of means provided by science and technology. There is another way of looking at that million years of human evolution which leads us almost directly to the one possibility of success. Man's basic instinctive drives may have remained the same throughout his evolution, but his neural machinery for carrying them into effect improved immensely. Brain size doubled during the period and almost all that increase was due to enlargement of the neopallium, the thinking portion of his brain. Man learnt to think of the future and to fear death, two wholly human attributes. Over the whole history of civilization and right up to the present his broad instinct-based patterns of behaviour have not changed. But his intelligence, the power to manipulate information, that was once the function of the neopallium alone, has been progressively enlarged. Language, the written word, printing and the dissemination of scholarly and technical information in books, mathematics and other types of symbolic formulation, as in chemistry and genetics, the processes of handling information were improved steadily over the centuries. The greatest of all the extensions of human intelligence—something which can be thought of as a major step in human evolution—is that provided by the electronic computer. Completely new horizons have appeared with the advent of this modern descendant of Babbage's Analytical Engine and its perfection, elaboration and commercial production in the last twenty years.

Computers are very much the fashion amongst scientists and ambitious young business-men to allow them to do the same sort of things they did before, but much more quickly and more accurately. This, in itself, may not be particularly important, but sometimes it has made possible calculations that were previously quite impossible and so added a qualitatively new facet to scholarship. What represents the evolutionarily significant development, the most significant extension of the function of the neopallium, as it were, is its application to man himself. The intelligent handling of information about human beings has really only become possible since we had the electronic data-processing machines. If ever we reach that global ecosystem, it will be because computers have made the detailed planning that will be necessary, a physically possible task. Unless the worst happens, computer techniques, and what grows from them, will be part of the equipment of the human species as long as it persists on earth, and, hopefully, their most important continuing function will be to guide our maintenance of the biosphere.

But an indefinitely viable world is still far away and the computers are equally potent for evil as for good. It is as well to remember that ENIAC, the first electronic computer, completed in 1946, was primarily designed for the calculation of the trajectories of bombs and shells. It is equally significant that the whole pattern of modern genocidal war has only been made possible by computer techniques. Every weapon is double-edged. The computer, like the neopallium itself, is no more than a tool for the accomplishment of ends which in the last analysis are generated in those ancient centres of the brain that are concerned with the instinctive drives, love, hate, ambition, jealousy, and the rest. Computers will not make science and technology capable of solving our human predicament. Something more is needed if this planet is to become a tolerable and continuing home for the human species. The concept itself and the will to bring it into being must be implanted in the minds of the significant men and women who make the decisions that matter in the world. Only when they are convinced will the computers be set on the task of planning and creating the global ecosystem.

In the next and final chapter we look at those trends already visible in human thought and behaviour which give some hope that the ideas *are* spreading and may be implemented in time.

ten   IN THE END: HOPE?

When I started to map out this rewriting of DM, I was very much aware of both the need for, and the difficulty of ever attaining the stable human ecosystem of my dreams. I had no clear idea, in fact, just what the tone of my last chapter would be. Would it be hopeful of global stability being well under way within, say, one hundred years, or would I have decided that the future was so sinister that the book should not even be completed? It has not worked out in either fashion. All that I have tried to express in terms of human biology, about man's history and current situation, makes it seem very unlikely that any stable solution will come as the happy climax of our first round of scientific civilization. Yet, like Boswell's friend who tried to be a philosopher, I find cheerfulness, not always, but occasionally breaking in.

I cannot pass over as unimportant the simple fact that in writing this book I am trying hard to *do* something to help lift the menace that hangs over us. So, each in his own way, have dozens of other men of goodwill.

Scientists have been conspicuous in such writing, and the *Bulletin of the Atomic Scientists*, for the last twenty years, has been their mouthpiece. The scientists have found allies in many other fields to support their analyses and protests against the three most visible evils—war, over-population and environmental deterioration. Not much has yet been achieved, but there are certainly large numbers of people on the side of the angels. As a biologist, I should be as active in looking for reasons why we are on the side of the angels as I have been in trying to understand the eternal dominance of the power addicts and war-makers in the human story.

There is another feature of the twentieth century which should also be examined for any gleams of hope. It is usually referred to as the call for social justice. There have always been large under-privileged groups, and there have been slave rebellions, revolts and mutinies throughout history. More frequently, power addicts have seen opportunity in the discontent of under-privileged groups to seize power for themselves. All this fits into the standard pattern of human behaviour and brings no hope. What may be new is that nowadays the active supporters of the minority groups include many from affluent homes. The Civil Rights movement in support of US negroes, the Peace Corps, and equivalent projects in England, Australia and elsewhere, brought many young people, often at the cost of real personal discomfort and danger, into active help for disadvantaged people and the under-developed countries. Nothing is, of course, all black and white. No elderly academic can be fully sympathetic with much of the current wave of student protest. One must, however, recognize that a significant part of student political activity is in seeking social justice for disadvantaged minorities. Something is working here which gives grounds for hope.

Finally, one must not forget the work being done by religious organizations. Religion, in the conventional sense, is disappearing rapidly in all educated communities, but it still has plenty of power to influence conservative and illiterate populations and, where circumstances allow intensive childhood indoctrination, it may continue to survive for centuries. Judaism, Christianity, Islam and Marxism have all been characteristically associated with aggressive military activity and intolerance. Christianity, however, has always had individuals and small initially heretical groups who worked for the Kingdom of Heaven on earth. Their motives may be as mixed as those of the usually agnostic student activists, but they must equally be included amongst those whose actions give some cause for hope.

In summary, there is a lot of goodwill and altruism in the world and some capacity for self-denial and even martyrdom in a good cause. These qualities must have an evolutionary background, as well as more immediate social origins. It may be that the same sort of biological enquiry as has been used to understand the bases of conflict may be applied to the co-operative aspects of human behaviour with benefit.

Anyone who has ever enjoyed the company of a dog is completely certain that the dog positively likes him. There is no other possible interpretation of the wagging tail, the eager approach and the pleasure of contact. The dog feels what we experience as affection and it is equally apparent that he needs to recognize affection toward him on the part of his owner. Those who have had to handle young chimpanzees tell us that these are even more dependent than dogs on being able to receive and give affection. I have never worked with chimpanzees, but at one time I became extremely interested in the evidence that they can be carriers of human hepatitis viruses. Around 1960, in the first stages of the American space programme, NASA needed rather large numbers of chimpanzees. They were obtained in the only 'practical' way to obtain a baby chimpanzee, by shooting the mother in Africa and getting the baby to a primate centre in Florida as swiftly as possible. Once there, it was found essential, if the baby chimps were to survive, to have a young woman, one for each baby, to look after its needs and, above all, to give it the 'tender loving care', the affection that it needed. My professional interest came into the story only because, after a month or two on the job, most of the nurse-maids came down with infectious jaundice from the virus the chimps were carrying.

Affection for their young is universal amongst the larger mammals, and one can probably look to the parent-offspring relationship for the basis of most of the affectionate, humanitarian and co-operative relationships amongst men and women. Affection is also evident as part of the mutual bond between a mated pair, at least of some species of mammals.

It is clear enough that behaviour, the outward form of which indicates that it is accompanied by what we feel as affection, is common or universal in mammals and has arisen for manifest evolutionary ends. One can, however, go rather more deeply than this by looking at physiological correlates of behaviour we interpret as affectionate. From this angle, we can think of affection as being associated with any sort of bodily contact that fulfils a normal biological function, suckling and protecting the young, mating, contact for mutual warmth and, in some species, the contact of individuals presenting a common front to a predator.

Amongst civilized people, bodily contact beyond the formal handshake is only acceptable when there is mutual affection. A young child has often to spend a long time before he will 'thaw' sufficiently to sit on a strange adult's knee. The normal process of courtship involves, and its progress can be gauged by the increasing extent and confidence of bodily contact from the slight prolongation of handshake to the final contact of intercourse. Affection is not necessarily or usually between equals—the proto-type is the mother-child relationship—but the superior-inferior relationship must be mutually acceptable if contact is not to be resented. Anyone who has a temperament that keeps him low in the peck-order will have been annoyed and embarrassed by the pat on the back or the clasp round the shoulders of the confident, friendly extrovert whom one neither likes nor feels inferior to. Yet, the same actions by the right person can be intensely gratifying. From our particular point of view, the ways in which affection is affected by superiority-inferiority relation-ships are of particular importance. In writing about this, I shall make considerable use of what I wrote in 1947, because I believe that it represents one of the more significant of the ideas I developed then.

From my own observation, most friendships among men re-quire a special type of mutual-dominance relationship. Each must excel in a field which does not bring him into competition with the other. Direct rivalry is not compatible with friendship or affection. An interesting example from fiction is to be found in Kipling's 'soldiers three', Mulvaney, Learoyd and Ortheris, all privates, and therefore socially equal, but each with his own in-dividual quality that can win admiration and with it affection from the others. Of a different order is the reciprocal relationship of leader and follower, master and servant, in fully stabilized communities. Here the rank relation allows liking or affection, but not friendship. Proverbial examples are the mutual affection of the king for his fool, the colonel for his batman, and the white mistress for her negro cook.

Affection is only stable if it is reciprocal, and the repulse of proffered affection can be deeply resented. Hell has no fury like a woman scorn'd—and this can hold in other fields than the sexual one. It may well point to one of the basic requirements for stability within any pyramid of authority. A man accepts the position of an inferior more happily if he has a liking for his immediate superior, and this is only likely to persist if he can feel that the liking is reciprocated at a personal level. In Shakespeare's picture of Henry the Fifth as the idealized military leader this aspect is strongly painted. 'Once more unto the breach, dear friends'; 'We few, we happy few, we band of brothers'. It is part of the tradition of political and military authority that the successful leader is one who can meet one of his least important supporters on terms that will make the little man feel that he is appreciated and liked. It is prescribed for every politician by his PR adviser and, in its modern form, it determines the image the polician tries to present on television.

Politics and public-relations may represent a mass of hypocrisy and make-believe, but it is only by such activities that the conflict-ridden communities of men manage to get the work of the world done with a minimum of violence. The goodwill, real or synthetic, of the general or politician is directed toward people whose support is essential to him, but the attitude can be extended beyond this. No political group could nowadays ever say publicly that it was not committed to the philosophy that every human being is in some sense equal to every other and entitled in full to certain basic human rights. A human biologist is generally more interested in human differences than in common qualities, but, just as much as the politician, he would strongly support the right of every individual to health, education and opportunity. Humanitarianism goes deeper than this, and perhaps the most

valid claim that can be made for the past importance and future
necessity of Christianity is its doctrine and practice of charity.
The religious man can assert that what distinguishes the good
man from the bad is his capacity for charity toward the sick and
deformed, the poor and the old, the evil and the undeserving.
Perhaps the most pertinent question that the Christian can ask
of the biologist is where such charity can be found elsewhere in
Nature. The biologist must confess that, as far as the point has
been discussed, any standard mammalian group is intolerant of
the unfit. I first realized this from reading a vivid description by
Francis Ratcliffe of how a 'mad' bullock was maltreated by the
rest of the herd on a Queensland cattle-station:

> 'When we returned to the yards we found his sides a mass of
> deep gashes. One of his attackers had managed to tear open
> the inside of his thigh, while the horn of another had actually
> penetrated the anus. The leader in the persecution seemed to
> be a particularly sleek and handsome beast. . . . The whole
> thing was too horribly human . . . The victim was so un-
> aggressively egregious, a bovine pacifist perhaps: his tor-
> mentors were such well-bred gentlemen (trust their breeder
> for that), so clearly Public School and "Varsity".'

Men, and particularly boys, can be intolerably cruel to an
outsider, but kindliness and humanitarianism are just as much
facts of human life. To me, at least, it was interesting to speculate
about what a strictly biological approach could do to account for
what theologians have tended to see as the most important,
perhaps the only manifestation of the divine in man. Being wholly
human means being able to use language and to verbalize
thought, and this must soon have brought primitive man to the
point at which he could take thought for the future and picture
his own old age and death. When illness, injury, coma or death
overtook one of his companions, he alone amongst mammals
could think that this might happen to him. It is a sound instinct
of self-protection to shun the sick, which means that men tend to
feel fear and disgust at the sight of serious illness or injury. Yet

there is also the instinct, never quite lost, to care for a sick or hungry child.

Religions have always been much concerned with sickness and death. Perhaps mainly from the need of maintaining some vestige of control over those in the seats of military and legal power, priests have always stressed the transience of health, of temporal dominion, and of life itself. In the background, too, there were beliefs from primitive cultures, which persisted for centuries, that the dead in some form of continuing existence might harm the living. This provided a further reason for kindliness to the dying, so that when dead they should harbour no inconvenient resentments against their relatives or other members of the community! Once thought for the future became a mammalian possibility, it was biologically necessary that ways should be found to overcome the instinctive revulsion from sickness and deformity. There are special features of Christianity in this regard. It began as a proletarian religion, and much of its attraction to early Christians may have lain in its capacity to create for the underdog the sense that, in things that mattered, he was the equal or the superior of those who in the eyes of the world dominated or enslaved him. Only the poor, the meek and the unfortunate were fit for the Kingdom of Heaven—the rich man or the ruler would find it harder to enter than for a camel to go through the eye of a needle.

When Christianity became a ruling-class religion and created an elaborate hierarchy of its own, something of the traditions of its origin remained. Throughout ecclesiastical history there have been enthusiasts who have re-discovered that a special virtue attaches to those who suffer from disabilities in this world. Such men founded orders in which members would voluntarily accept poverty, chastity and obedience and, to the limit of their knowledge and opportunity, comfort the sick and the oppressed. Modern humanitarianism, at least in its Western guise, can probably said to be derived from Christian sources, notably the Benedictine and Franciscan orders. I like to think, however, that there were two additional sources that converged eventually with the Christian stream. The lay-doctors, barbers, tooth-pullers and quacks of the Middle Ages made their living by treating—and cheating—the sick. Amongst them, however, some were moved by compassion, and others began to feel the first stirrings of a scientific approach to disease. Profit, compassion and science eventually brought the medical profession into existence, to play its essential part in the development of an *effective* humanitarianism.

The other influence which should not be forgotten came from the ruling-classes, primarily in an attempt to diminish vagrancy and crime, but, again, compassion played a part. The provision of poor laws, almshouses, and so forth, was, in a sense, perhaps the fore-runner of the Welfare State. More realistically, we can look at the three streams, Christian charity, medical care for the sick, and shelter and food for the indigent, as fusing to give the modern Western approach to social security and the doctrine of basic human equality. Both are wholly human characteristics, but there is no need to seek any supernatural understanding of their origin.

In the world of 1969–70, there are all too many areas of human conflict, and in many of them there is very little that can be seized on as cause for optimism. Warlike conflict at international level in the day of the nuclear bomb has been dealt with in an earlier chapter—as far as it can be dealt with. Racial conflict seems to me a monster with no biological reality. Cross-mating between any two human races gives fertile offspring. Only in a few obscure and inhospitable regions of the world are there any populations which could claim to be 'pure' races. Characteristically, there is no sexual obstacle to cross-racial marriage or mating at either the highest or the lowest social level. Probably most successful cross-racial marriages are between people of high intellectual or artistic achievement. At the other level, there never was a conquering army that made no use of the women of the country, however different their colour. I do not believe that White-Negro differences in the United States are of any more significance than Catholic-Protestant differences in Ulster or in the religious wars of Uganda in 1892.

Probably the most currently interesting area of conflict from our point of view is that which involves the 'problems of youth'. They grow quite clearly out of the primary parent-child relationship. In infancy and early childhood the parent, and particularly the mother, is in a position of absolute dominance. This allows, and under normal conditions demands, altruism and affection from her in the highest degree. Affection on both sides probably reaches a peak when the child is two or three years old, still absolutely dependent but able to express reciprocated affection and happiness. As the child develops a 'will of its own' and begins to struggle against authority, parental affection is liable to lapse at times. With adolescence, difficulties become greater and, in due course, either at marriage or before, the young take on full adult responsibility. Throughout the process, personal goodwill and effort on both sides is needed to keep the relationship a basically happy one. As in all personal relationships, it helps if a father and adult son never find it necessary to compete with each other for opportunity or prestige in the same fields.

When people of my age-group look at the current twenty-year-olds, the generation gap looms unduly large. Some of the more visible of the young raise the hackles of the elderly with their beards and their manifest lack of what we thought of as self-respect and pride in one's appearance. Yet I know also that when I lecture to medical students nowadays, I find that more young people with keener minds come up afterwards to seek more enlightenment, or to disagree on some point, than was ever the case ten years ago. It is of the nature of our mass media to over-magnify the trend-setters, the militants, the delinquents and the criminals amongst the young. It is a small minority made too conspicuous. In a well-publicized sub-group of American young people there is a highly permissive attitude to sex and an eagerness to experiment with psychotropic drugs. The same phenomena seem to be spreading beyond America and can already be seen in Australia. More uniformly, throughout the Western countries, one finds an increasing proportion of criminal activity in people under twenty-five and a high proportion of young men amongst those responsible for fatal road accidents.

It may be inappropriate and unwise to pay undue attention to these conspicuous minorities, yet, in a sense, they merely manifest wider trends all of which seem to point in the same direction. There is a desire to underline, rather offensively in both senses of the word, their refusal to accept dominance by parents and by the culture they identify with their parents. It may be that this attitude has been accentuated in the 1960s by their sense of irrational and undeserved threat of annihilation by nuclear war. Others have suggested that the virtual disappearance of any interest in religion amongst educated people may have had an influence in the same direction. Life can easily be regarded as 'meaningless', in the sense that there is no longer a defined and fairly effective pattern of social structure and behaviour with strong inhibitions against anti-social behaviour—and supernatural post-mortem reward or punishment for one's actions is certainly not now relevant. So we find a hedonistic, existentialist culture in which the immediately gratifying and exciting things are primarily sought—money and a sense of power, sex, alcohol, speed and drugs. It is obvious that, without the modern additions of speed and psychotropic drugs, young people have always been interested in these things. It is equally true that a majority of the current young are making as satisfactory adjustment to adult life as any of their predecessors. The minority, however, seems much more conspicuous than the non-conformers of previous generations.

Basically, the same attitudes are associated with student revolt in the universities, but here there are additional factors and potentialities and a basically new situation has arisen since 1947. Then there was no sign in Western universities of anything remotely resembling the 'student revolt' of the late 1960s. The universities everywhere were crowded with ex-servicemen making up for time lost during the war. They were more mature than the standard university student and, in Australia at least, they were serious-minded, hard-working and basically conformist.

Since the Berkeley troubles of 1964 became generally known throughout the Western world, almost every non-communist country has had outbreaks of student disobedience and violence of varying intensity. In any discussion of conflict, or of the possibilities of eliminating the occasion for war, some notice must be taken of this social phenomenon. There has been no word of student unrest in any of the communist countries, presumably because of the discipline exerted by a combination of childhood indoctrination and the absolute control by the State of both educational and job opportunities. By contrast, in America, where student revolt has provided great research material for sociologists, the activists differ categorically from USSR students in both respects. According to the surveys, most student activists come from upper middle-class homes where they have had a relatively permissive upbringing by liberally minded parents; they have been well educated and are intelligent enough to be accepted by universities as selective as Harvard or the Sorbonne. Our three biological rules (p. 122) have been applied in their upbringing.

The next point of general application is that there are extremely few students from the sciences, or the applied sciences, in the politically active minorities. Students, whether in the humanities or the sciences, with ambition for professional success or a scholar's interest in their subjects are not found in their ranks. Students of the social sciences make up the majority of the rebels, and one gains the impression that the leaders of revolt tend to be highly intelligent young men who have chosen university programmes which they can count on passing with a minimum of effort.

There seem to be two ostensible reasons for revolt, the prominence of which varies from one centre to another. There are usually some weaknesses in university curricula or methods which are against the students' interests and provide legitimate reasons for protest. One gathers that in France, Germany and Japan, university facilities were quite inadequate for the numbers of students, as judged by American or even Australian standards. In any university there will be something to complain about, but this seems to have been quite an unimportant factor in most American disturbances.

The most frequently stated reason throughout the Western

world is to foster revolutionary action by students and workers. A university is a traditional institution which from its nature is readily disorganized by disruptive action. By rendering first the universities, and then other institutions of current society unworkable, the activists claim they will provide the conditions for a revolutionary socialism of Marxist- or Maoist-type to be set up in its place. What is conspicuously lacking is any serious effort to work out the actual form of the society the rebels are aiming at. It seems more likely that the chief attraction of revolt is the immature fascination of conspiring to flout authority, with the certainty in the modern world that any violence induced will be reported and exaggerated in the mass media. The first rule is to demonstrate against anything that comes readily to hand in the hope of provoking police action to break up the demonstration under the eye of the television cameras. Once this stage has been reached, mass hysteria is readily generated amongst the more simple-minded of the non-activist majority and the trouble builds up in an exasperatingly meaningless fashion. A university, being traditionally organized as an orderly community in which status is reached by scholarship rather than by capacity to exert authority, nearly always fumbles badly in handling its troubles.

One of the reasons that makes it difficult to rewrite DM with anything like my initial enthusiasm is one's increasing consciousness of the role of the irrational and the psychopathic in creating political and social climates. It is characteristic that the liberally minded scientific approach to the future that H. G. Wells implanted in the thinking of my own generation is anathema to student activists. My own approach is very much in the Wellsian tradition. It is common for both the scholarly sociologist and the revolutionary student to call that attitude naïve in the extreme. The scholars are concerned essentially with things as they are and with projection of current processes into the future. The revolutionists amongst the students take their lead from current revolutionary techniques in under-developed countries and flatly reject reasonable compromise and the progressive *ad hoc* solution of difficulties as they arise. Violence, in one form or another, is the primary requirement. Student protest in the West has generated violence at only a trivial level, but it has important associations with the other more lethal revolutionary movements of our time. Some recent interpretations of the technique of the Cuban Revolution and its attempted application to other South American countries are of special interest in relation both to student protest and to the general attitude I adoped toward human conflict in Chapters Three and Four.

According to such analyses as that of Lowenthal, the modern revolutionary philosophy as presented by Marcuse, Guevara, Mao, etc., differs essentially from that of the Russian Revolution by discarding any pretence that revolution is part of a historical situation leading logically to increased productivity by the application of science to industry and eventually to a tolerable living for all. The classical Marxist doctrine was that once modest affluence had been reached under the dictatorship of the proletariat, the way would open for the equally inevitable 'withering away' of the State and the appearance of a communist Utopia in which there would be no cause for human conflict and no necessity for repressive authority.

The modern approach is not based on reason. Its doctrine is that in an under-developed country where there is resentment and frustration in large under-privileged groups and a visible ruling-class enemy, the primary requirement for revolution is simply the initiation and extension of violence. It is unnecessary and dangerous to present a reasoned reformist case for the remedy of felt evils. Adequate violence will eventually give rise to a revolutionary situation which will develop under its own momentum. What is needed is a socially conditioned group of adolescent and young adult males who can be persuaded to enjoy the pleasure and power of killing, a charismatic leader and some sketch of a Utopia as a nominal objective. 'Charismatic leader' can be equated with a power-seeking opportunist rendered psychopathically addicted to power by some initial success. It is entirely in accord with our analysis of human evolution that revolutionary leaders of the type of Castro, Guevara, Mao, the men who were responsible for Mau Mau terrorism, and all the lesser architects of human misery should find no difficulty in building up their armies of devoted unthinking killers, almost all of them immature males. One likely interpretation of the 1966 Great Cultural Revolution in China was Mao's nostalgia for the guerilla activities of his past, for an attitude contrasting strongly with the inevitable institutionalization of society into a working organism that was taking place under his eyes. As a substitute for outright guerilla activity and in the absence of any really appropriate enemy, a lower-level activity with much bearing on the pattern of Western student revolt was initiated. The enemy was the developing communist bureaucracy with its understandable activity in building a Russian-style industrial state that could offer a progressive increase in living-standards. The guerilla forces again were immature males given, not lethal weapons, but a queer sort of authority to enjoy the power of interfering with their own education and with any manifestations of social organization which did not seem to them in line with primitive revolutionary morality. As far as one can judge, the result has been to slow down China's economic development and to increase greatly the power of the army.

Returning to the student situation in the West, this has so far not lead to serious political consequences. Student frustration and resentment has quite inadequate intensity and there is a large element of make-believe in the manifestations. What may be important, however, is the theoretical rejection of the method of 'piecemeal social engineering' as the standard approach to reform, and the adoption by students (and many other minority groups) of menacing postures over what are essentially trivial matters. Another point, which may not be particularly important but which is irritating to a realist, is the apparent inability of the proponents of revolution to recognize that the standard of living they enjoy, and accept as given, is only possible in a technologically advanced and disciplined society.

From the point of view of a human biologist seeking ways to counter irrational protest and violence, the need is to find ways by which biologically or socially desirable changes can be implemented without violence. I have, in at least two contexts, already indicated that effective persuasion must be by and

toward the élite—the educated intelligent responsible people
who alone can change the way things are.

But one must have sympathy with the young and impatient.
They are exasperated by the innate conservatism of most people
and particularly of those in positions of influence which could be
threatened by the desirable change. They are not the first and
will not be the last generation to fume at the law's delay, the
insolence of office, and the rest. These things have been with us
since the beginnings of civilization.

It is axiomatic that any group of people who can be persuaded
to feel that they are being unjustly treated will seek means of
redressing the injustice, and that the means used will be those
customary in their particular community. Justice is a word which
is notoriously flexible, but, objectively considered, a man feels
that he suffers from injustice when circumstances force him to
accept a place in some hierarchy which he and his peers consider
is lower than he should expect. If one accepts the approach I
tried to develop in Chapter Three, effective administration of
any industrial or other organization necessitates the maintenance
of a pyramid of authority. People must be sorted into the levels
of the hierarchy with a minimum of felt and expressed resentment. They must feel that, by and large, they have been justly
treated. The primary task of the activist, the trouble-maker, is
to persuade people that they have been unjustly treated, to
exacerbate minor difficulties in ranking, or exploit major ones to
disrupt the organization. There is no simple answer—the situation
is exactly similar to the classical difficulties of wage-fixing and
job relativity in industrial relations. They can never be solved,
but at least understanding and goodwill can do something to
make the necessary decisions more acceptable.

In one way or another, we must hold up our heads and hope, no
matter how heavy are the odds against that dream of SHEFTE.
We have only to ask a few realistic questions to fell how thin are
the prospects. What can be done to weaken the influence of the
men in power in the Pentagon or its equivalent for the other
great powers, of the heads of science-based industry, the

distributors of arms, and all the others with a direct interest in preparation for war and the prevention of disarmament? How are we going to answer politicians and profit-makers who claim that any respect for the environment or any slow-down of the bombardment of advertisements can only be done at the cost of that sacred figure, the rate of national growth? How do we teach the elements of human ecology to the Church hierarchies, to the imams, qadis and muftis of Islam, to the nationalistic heads of new African States. Finally, at a very different but in its own way an equally important level, what do we do about the slovenly woman with an IQ of eighty, usually of some under-privileged racial or economic group who produces yearly children in some derelict shanty town? The answer to all of them is: Nothing effective—*yet*.

But the same answer could once have been given about gladiatorial combat, judicial and ecclesiastical torture, capital punishment, the slave-trade, child labour, or massive infantile mortality. All those things have gone because small groups of highly intelligent men, almost all of the upper social classes, were secure enough to have charity for the unfortunate and had leisure enough to write and speak for the reforms they championed. Always it was a long, slow process of education, limited at first to the privileged élite. Only when that was accomplished was it ready for the people to hear, understand and, in the end, sweep the infamy away.

A few years ago, I acted as host to a dinner tendered by a group of Melbourne academics to the late Sir Charles Darwin. After dinner, he talked to us of the pattern of human destiny as he saw it. He was not optimistic, and when the evening was over and I was seeing him to his car he asked me a question, the content and tone of which I shall never forget: 'Burnet, do you think any *good* can ever come out of it all?' He would have liked to hear some sort of an affirmative answer and, in something more than a trivial sense, this book has been an attempt to answer that question.

The human predicament, the whole fate of the species is more desperate now than it has ever been, but there is still one great ground for hope. The educated élite, the men who can sufficiently shake off their childhood indoctrination to understand the nature of current evils, is also larger than it has ever been. It is active everywhere; signs of movement can be seen in the Catholic Church, in the literary and scientific worlds of the USSR, amongst Islamic scholars. In the West, ideas spread more readily than in any previous time. We are bombarded with information from every direction, but one of the wonderful things about the human brain is its power of selective attention. With effort, one can filter what is meaningful out of a vast volume of 'noise'— the physicists' twist to that word has added something vital to the English language—and the sort of ideas I have been writing about are spreading fast. Science still has prestige, and not only because it is the goose that lays golden eggs for business-men and atom bombs for the military. Its influence on the thinking of the younger generation may turn out to be crucial. One of our main responsibilities as scientists is to pass on to successive generations of students and junior colleagues the quality of the scientific method, the approach to research and, equally importantly, the ways to reach and use established knowledge. At every point we must stress the fact that knowledge grows progressively, that in science every 'truth' is subject to continuing scrutiny and must be modified or replaced as soon as a consensus of informed opinion calls for the change. There are no eternal verities.

As teachers we have one immense advantage over most others, that whether we are simple or sophisticated, superbly intelligent, or just run-of-the-mill, we can believe everything we teach. The young can recognize integrity, or its absence, in their teachers. They are likely to respond even more positively to the third main function of science—the one with which I have been chiefly concerned—an over-riding care for the human environment and for our destiny as a species.

Our dream of a global ecosystem differs only in one essential way from all the Utopias since Plato's Republic. It is more deeply based on an understanding of the biology of man. As that understanding extends, the dream will take firmer shape and if ever it should be realized, it will survive.

May I end by summarizing almost all that I have said in one sentence:

A viable and humanly tolerable world—a stable human ecosystem for the earth—is conceptually, ecologically and socially possible, but it will not be reached unless men and women of vision, purpose and intelligence can devise ways of controlling, modifying and redirecting those patterns of behaviour that were consolidated in the course of human evolution and which have brought us to the brink of chaos.

BIBLIOGRAPHY

The reading on which this book is based has been spread over most of a lifetime. The influence of H. G. Wells is plain to see; so is the effect of fifty years' browsing in *Nature* and *The Lancet*. Here I am doing little more than listing a group of fairly recent books that have, in one way or another, influenced my point of view, or which seem to offer the reader enlightenment on some of the themes I have treated.

Allee, Warder C. & others *Principles of Animal Ecology*. repr. Saunders, Philadelphia, 1950.

Ardrey, Robert *African Genesis: A Personal Investigation into the Animal Origins and Nature of Man*. Collins, London, 1961.

The Territorial Imperative: A Personal Inquiry into the Animal Origins of Property and Nations. Collins, London, 1967.

Carthy, John D. & Ebling, Francis J. G. *The Natural History of Aggression*. Proceedings of a Symposium held at the British Museum (Natural History), London, 21-22 October 1963 and published for the Institute of Biology by Academic Press, London, 1964.

Ciba Foundation *Conflict in Society*. A Ciba Foundation volume, edited by Anthony de Reuck & Julie Knight. Churchill, London, 1966.

Health of Mankind. A Ciba Foundation volume, edited by Gordon Wolstenholme & Maeve O'Connor. Churchill, London, 1968.

Man and his Future. A Ciba Foundation volume, edited by Gordon Wolstenholme, Churchill, London, 1963.

Gabor, Dennis *Inventing the Future.* Secker & Warburg, London, 1963.

Gardner, Robert & Heider, Karl G. *Gardens of War: Life and Death in the New Guinea Stone Age.* Andre Deutsch, London, 1969.

Harrison, Geoffrey A. & others *Human Biology: An Introduction to Human Evolution, Variation and Growth.* Oxford University Press, London, 1964.

Hinde, Robert A. *Animal Behaviour: A Synthesis of Ethology and Comparative Psychology.* McGraw-Hill, New York, 1966.

Keith, Arthur *A New Theory of Human Evolution.* Watts, London, 1948.

Keynes, John Maynard *The General Theory of Employment, Interest and Money.* Macmillan, London, 1936.

Koestler, Arthur *The Act of Creation.* Hutchinson, London, 1964. *The Ghost in the Machine.* Hutchinson, London, 1967.

Lorenz, Konrad Z. *King Solomon's Ring: New Light on Animal Ways.* Methuen, London, 1952. *On Aggression.* Methuen, London, 1966.

Medawar, Peter B. *The Art of the Soluble.* Methuen, London, 1967.

Montagu, Montague F. A. *Man and Aggression.* Oxford University Press, New York, 1968.

Morris, Desmond *The Naked Ape: A Zoologist's Study of the Human Animal.* Jonathan Cape, London, 1967.

Popper, Karl R. *Conjectures and Refutations: The Growth of Scientific Knowledge.* Routledge & Kegan Paul, London, 1963.

Ratcliffe, Francis N. *Flying Fox and Drifting Sand: The Adventures of a Biologist in Australia.* Chatto & Windus, London, 1938.

Richardson, Lewis F. *Statistics of Deadly Quarrels*; edited by Q. Wright & C. C. Lienau. Stevens, London, 1960.

Schaller, George B. *The Year of the Gorilla.* University of Chicago Press, Chicago, 1964.

Sheldon, William H. & Stevens, Stanley S. *Varieties of Tempera-*
ment: A Psychology of Constitutional Differences. Harper &
Row, New York, 1942.
Wynne-Edwards, Vero C. *Animal Dispersion in Relation to*
Social Behaviour. Oliver & Boyd, Edinburgh, 1962.

Specific reference is also made to three of my own writings,
including some substantial quotations. These are:

Burnet, F. Macfarlane *Biology and the Appreciation of Life.*
Sun Books, Melbourne, 1968.
Changing Patterns: An Atypical Autobiography. Heinemann,
Melbourne, 1968; reprinted Sun Books, Melbourne, 1970.
Immunological Surveillance. Pergamon Press, Sydney, 1970.

INDEX